Rewilding
the Sea

Rewilding the Sea

How to Save
Our Oceans

CHARLES CLOVER

WITNESS
BOOKS

1

Witness Books, an imprint of Ebury Publishing,
20 Vauxhall Bridge Road,
London SW1V 2SA

Witness Books is part of the Penguin Random House group of companies
whose addresses can be found at global.penguinrandomhouse.com

Penguin
Random House
UK

First published in the United Kingdom by Witness Books in 2022

Maps and illustrations © Emily Faccini 2022

Epigraph on p. xi © Ian Tyson, reproduced with permission

www.penguin.co.uk

A CIP catalogue record for this book is available from the British Library

ISBN 9781529144031

Typeset in 12.75/18.5pt Garamond MT Std by Jouve (UK), Milton Keynes.

Printed and bound in Great Britain by Clays Ltd, Elcograf S.p.A.

The authorised representative in the EEA is Penguin Random House Ireland,
Morrison Chambers, 32 Nassau Street, Dublin D02 YH68

Penguin Random House is committed to a sustainable future for
our business, our readers and our planet. This book is made from
Forest Stewardship Council® certified paper.

This book is dedicated to the memory of Dave Sales, 1937–2022, and to those like him who have opted to fish less in order to have more.

Contents

INTRODUCTION

Return of the Giants

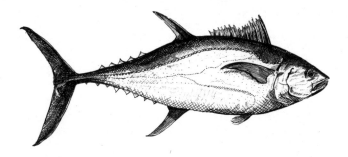

'Four strong winds that blow lonely
Seven seas that run high
All those things that don't change, come what may'

Ian Tyson, 'Four Strong Winds', 1961

ST. KILDA AND HARRIS

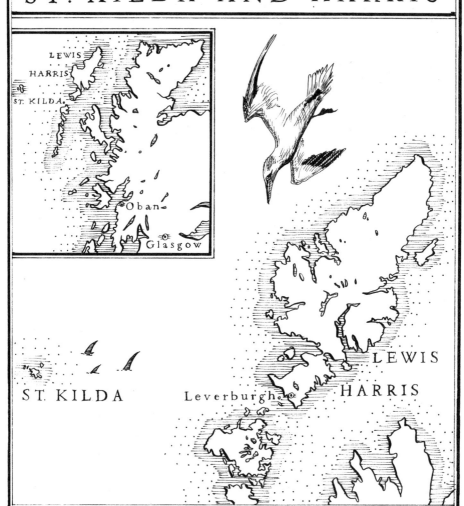

LEWIS
HARRIS
ST. KILDA.

Oban

Glasgow

ST. KILDA

Leverburgh

LEWIS

HARRIS

The day of Tom Horton's first encounter with the creature he was looking for was misty and overcast with not a breath of wind. The sea off the west of Scotland was oil-slick calm, moved only by a slight swell from far out in the Atlantic. Tom had motored out 40 miles to the remote islands of St Kilda from the village of Leverburgh, on the Isle of Harris, on Angus Campbell's catamaran, the *Orca 3*. It was September 2014 and they were on a mission to find and tag a bluefin tuna, a year after Angus had first spotted the shoals, prepared a squid lure and caught one weighing 515lbs, a Scottish record. Bluefin had not been seen in any numbers in this part of the north-east Atlantic for decades. Angus was the first to spot them and work out how to catch one. Marine Scotland, part of the Scottish government, then decided to record what was happening and recruited Tom as a volunteer.

The day had already been memorable for wildlife spotting. As Tom and Angus started out, they saw a pod of around 200 dolphins, far off. Then, on the journey between the Isle of Harris and St Kilda, a juvenile male minke whale circled their boat. They also sighted a sei whale as it rolled in the distance and a leatherback turtle lazing at the surface close by. As Tom said, it was a day when you felt something big was about to happen.

They were motoring back towards Harris, around two o'clock, out of sight of land, when Angus said: 'This is what we are looking for.'

Coming into view was a maelstrom of bird activity – gannets mostly but also bonxies (great skuas), sooty shearwaters, Manx shearwaters and storm petrels milling around. The gannets were diving into shoals of fish while the shearwaters darted between picking scraps off the surface. The bonxies were being their usual nuisance to the other birds. The water was so clear that you could see the birds swimming below the surface. The sea was glistening with slowly sinking silvery scales from the baitfish that had been forced to the surface by predators beneath, only to be picked off by the birds. Tom spotted numerous minke whales foraging on the shoals of baitfish.

Angus was certain there were bluefin present. Tom thought he was mistaken. Then, out of nowhere, a shoal popped up right in front of the boat. At first there were welts in the water and dorsal fins visible above the silvery surface. Then two large tuna surfaced five metres in front of the boat and dived back down underneath it, close enough for Tom to get four pictures that proved without doubt what they were seeing was bluefin. It all happened so quickly. The gannets were calling, the sooty shearwaters were whooshing, then the boat was through the feeding frenzy and the fish had moved on.

Tom and Angus were privileged to gain a glimpse of the part predators play in a fully functioning ecosystem, a sight unfamiliar until the wild and dynamic element of a bluefin shoal returned to northern seas. The tuna rounded up their prey of small fish – probably whitebait or herring fry – into tight shoals or balls and pushed these up to the surface. This provided a feeding bonanza for birds that cannot dive for fish, such as the petrels and the skuas which just steal prey from others. The petrels and skuas are rare now, rarer than when there were more large predators in the ocean, and so it is true to say that the bluefin are breathing life back into the whole system. In a real but unquantifiable way, they have rewilded it.

Seven years later and Tom has logged over 2,000 sightings of bluefin shoals in UK and Irish waters, in the Hebrides, in the Celtic Sea and off Falmouth. He is based at Exeter University's campus at Falmouth in Cornwall and the paper of which he is the lead author records with authority that 'Atlantic bluefin tuna returned to the English Channel from 2014 onwards, seasonally between August and December, after a prolonged absence.'

The Atlantic migrants had not been seen in UK waters since shoals of giant 'tunny' fish, as they were then called, preyed on herring in the North Sea off Scarborough in the 1920s and 1930s. These giant fish of 800lb or more were pursued by big-game fishermen from high society and film stars such as John Wayne, Errol Flynn and David Niven. The huge North Sea herring shoals that lured them there have since gone but there is plenty of sardine and anchovy in the warming waters of the English Channel and right out to the edge of the continental shelf to attract the foraging tuna. Now there are days in the Channel and the Celtic Sea, says Tom, where everywhere you look there's a bluefin.

The giants have returned. Why have these emperors among fish, their flesh so highly prized for sushi and sashimi in Japan and the Far East, surged back into north European waters after so many decades of plummeting towards extinction? Scientists say that several factors may be involved: the changing climate, the abundance of prey and – the most likely overall explanation for the bluefin's expansion northwards – the growing size of the population.

Creatures expand their range when there are more of them – that is a well-established pattern in ecology. The bluefin fits that pattern. This means that the crucial factor in the bluefin's return is the decision by Atlantic, Mediterranean and Far Eastern nations to stop overfishing the species and to crack down on illegal fishing in a series of steps from 2010. This stands out as one of the great conservation achievements of this century.

It took a decade or more of orchestrating public outrage about overfishing, which I had some part in, before the much-criticised International Commission for the Conservation of Atlantic Tunas (ICCAT), the regional fisheries management organisation for the Atlantic, finally made the right decision. Two of its most recalcitrant players, the European Union and Japan, came under pressure and reluctantly gave in. ICCAT took its decision late, when catches had been far too high and when the bluefin was sliding towards extinction. The EU finally succumbed to pressure, cut the fishing season around the spawning shoals in the Mediterranean by three quarters and then stamped down on illegal fishing. And nature, too, gave the bluefin a lucky break. The critical year of 2010 was followed by several good years for the survival of bluefin eggs and larvae and, under far lighter fishing pressure, the population began to rocket upwards. The result is a message of hope: conservation works. As Tom put it: 'When we get good-news stories like these we should shout to the ceiling about them. It means "we can do this", rather than "everything in the natural world is knackered".'

He's right. The natural world is far more dynamic than we give it credit for, especially the sea. We know now that the recovery of the magnificent bluefin in the north-east Atlantic is a sign of hope, an example of what can be done to restore our seas, which have changed so much in a single lifetime, despite what the lyrics of that Ian Tyson song, most memorably sung by Neil Young,[1] might say. Recovery, though, is fragile, vulnerable to changes in the climate and needs to be supported relentlessly, year on year.

This book tells the story of how I journeyed from despair to hope about the state of our common oceans.[2] It is a tale of beginnings, of extraordinary changes achieved around the world by small bands of dedicated people. Here, you will find an account of how things once thought impossible have happened and which have led, in one way or another, to what I call rewilding the sea.

To rewild the sea is to bring back lost and depleted species to our oceans and restore ecosystems that have been harmed by human activities – simply by stepping back and letting nature repair the damage, or by reintroducing species or restoring habitats. To get to the point where that is possible, however, is usually far from simple: determined campaigning, political will and sometimes significant funding from government and other organisations are all required. But this is achievable and success is happening. Those examples of progress for which I have evidence and experience, were they to be replicated, might succeed on a far wider scale. Though it is true that the world's oceans have never faced more challenges – from ruthless overfishing, plastic pollution, climate change and acidification – there has not been a decade or so of change like the past one since the battle to save the great whales in the 1970s and 1980s.

There is now a clear alternative to depletion. Over-exploitation – de-wilding, you might call it – goes on but in various places around the world there is a fragile but strengthening pulse of positive achievements to be celebrated. A record number of steps have been taken to restore our depleted oceans by creating protected areas or insisting upon better management of populations of fish and other creatures. It has been a time of gradual changes that will roll on into the future. But there is so much more to be done. There is now an ambition expressed by more than 100 countries to protect a third of the ocean by 2030. There has been a measurable change in public consciousness that has quickened the pace of activity. There is also reason to hope that the new trends in human behaviour towards the sea are accelerating as we realise that the crises in the ocean and the atmosphere are linked and need to be tackled together. Indeed, it is no overstatement to say that we need to save the oceans to save our own life-support system.

This book is based on my experience as a writer and journalist and as one of a small crew of people who made a film of my previous book about the global problem of overfishing, *The End of the Line*. Thanks to the film's momentum and the determination and vision of George Duffield, one of its producers, and Chris Gorell Barnes, an executive producer, some of us then set up a new marine conservation charity, the Blue Marine Foundation (BLUE), in 2010. My colleagues at BLUE, who I will refer to as I go along in this book, have been champions of rewilding the sea – both in the UK and across the globe. It is also about the wider network of people we then worked with. Our film, *The End of the Line*, which we premiered at Sundance in 2009, directed by Rupert Murray, supported a successful campaign to save the bluefin tuna from extinction.

Thereafter, our first decade of activity launched with a bang. We had the idea of using private wealth to create the largest marine reserve in the world, in the Indian Ocean, and paid a government to do so for five years. Then we found ourselves amid a campaign to change the law to stop the overfishing of European seas. As an active member of a formidable coalition, the Great British Oceans coalition, we managed to persuade a British government to turn all 14 of its far-flung fragments of empire scattered across the ocean – subject to local support and environmental need – into huge marine sanctuaries known as the Blue Belt, the biggest network of protected areas on the planet.

Over the same period, some of us worked with fishermen to manage a marine protected area in British inshore waters that has seen an enormous revival of life. It shows that letting nature lead also works for fishermen and consumers. This model goes on working, finding adherents around the British coast and in the Mediterranean.

Now, in our second decade as a charity, we appear to have persuaded a post-Brexit UK government to obey its own laws and force the expulsion of bottom trawlers and dredgers from 5,400 square miles of the North Sea on Dogger Bank, supposedly a marine protected area, and from 39 other vast offshore 'protected areas' that, laughably, were not actually protected at all.

All these positive and hope-giving developments happened at a time when the world appeared to be facing a ghoulish parade of nightmare environmental challenges, from the climate crisis, which is already devastating the coral reefs, to the destruction of forests and animal species and the tide of plastic waste still entering the ocean. This book will show what determined individuals have done in projects and policies around the world to overturn some of the most significant problems humankind has caused in the ocean – in particular, the wiping out of sea life by one relatively small but ubiquitous industry, the industrial fishing industry.

Industrial fishing stands revealed as one of the greatest environmental problems on Earth: it is one of the most destructive of biological diversity and, ironically, of the food a growing human population needs. If that wasn't enough, it is accelerating significantly the other problem of the global commons: climate change. The carbon emissions from trawling were recently estimated as equivalent to the global aviation industry. Aviation emissions are an enormous and intractable problem, since no one can foresee people wanting to stop flying and the technology to produce planes that run on hydrogen or electricity is in its infancy. By contrast, overfishing and destructive fishing can be fixed, given determination and the right attitude of mind – and thanks to the extraordinary recuperative powers of nature.

Change is in the air partly because of inspiring examples of rewilding on land. The reintroduction of large, lost species such as beaver, oryx, wolf and bear has begun a discussion about doing the same things in the sea – where campaigns to save large, vulnerable species have been going on for some time. The oceans are larger, more dynamic and in common ownership, so the solutions are different. The oceans still have their megafauna – their whales, sharks and other large fish – but the areas allegedly protected for many of these creatures is pitifully small in relation to their needs. The goals of conservation in the ocean lag behind those on land. It was generally expected from around 1980 that civilised nations would set aside 10 per cent of their land area primarily for nature. In the world's oceans, only 8 per cent was protected by 2020. The ambition is now that we should protect 30 per cent of the global ocean by 2030.

But what does protection mean? We continue to apply terrestrial thinking to the sea – on land, we may safeguard 'features', like an orchid meadow or an ancient wood – rather than protecting dynamic and interrelated ecosystems for what they are in their entirety. Right now, some 97 per cent of protected areas in the UK are fished in some way and most are trawled. The total area fully protected from fishing and other extractive operations in England's waters is currently 16.4 sq kms, an area smaller than the City of Westminster. Our thinking is clearly unambitious. Where are the reserves for the megafauna of the sea, the sturgeons, the halibut, the skate and the angel sharks, not to mention the herring that the bluefin tuna once fed upon off European shores? What would the sea be like if they were there again? Why is trawling and dredging still allowed almost everywhere?

Despite the pulse of good news, for now, the official statistics on the oceans are gloomy. Globally, according to the records kept by the UN Food and Agriculture Organisation, the state of harvestable fish stocks continues to decline. In its latest assessment of the state of wild capture fisheries, the organisation conceded that some 94 per cent of all fish stocks were now either fully exploited or over-exploited, with the over-exploited element accounting for 34 per cent of the whole. Around the UK, populations of cod, the traditional choice for fish and chips, have collapsed and yet, as I write, the UK and EU fishing ministers have again set a level of catches well in excess of scientific advice, making it almost impossible for stocks to recover. The future is being sacrificed again for short-term profit – contrary to multiple commitments by both the UK and EU to rebuild stocks to healthy levels. Acceptance of this kind of decision-making still prevails in official quarters and it is relentlessly depressing.

Yet there is an awakening going on. The balance of opinion is shifting against industries that soak up public money, slaughter wildlife, emit carbon dioxide, deliver little benefit to the communities they claim to serve and often break the law. We have begun to realise that if we rewild the oceans by placing nature first, it will help us solve some of the other monumental and pressing problems we face, such as the climate crisis, by taking up more carbon from the atmosphere. Trusting nature to repair the damage we have done is a win, win, win – for wildlife, for people who love the sea, for fishermen and women and humanity as a whole. We just need to replicate the successes more often.

What does rewilding the sea look like? The definition I will use in this book is this: rewilding is any effort by anyone to improve the health of the oceans by actively restoring their habitats and species or by leaving them alone to recover. This is the widest possible definition but it is the right one, I believe, because it includes people of goodwill who manage parts of the ocean, work or fish in them, who protect habitats for nature conservation reasons or who set out to restore natural habitats that have been damaged or destroyed. All these beneficial activities constitute rewilding and these proponents of rewilding – whether or not they think of themselves in that way – need to work more in concert in the decades ahead. It will take patience, funding and political will – and perhaps a few short-term sacrifices – to make the greatest gains but I believe the idea of rewilding the sea is now established and brings hope for the future, for people and for nature.

1

Where the Wild Things Really Are

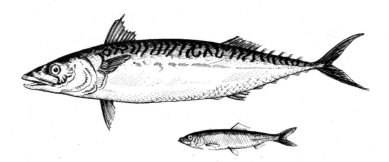

'The fish were divided into distinct columns, of five or six miles in length, and three or four broad. While the water before them curls up, as if forced out of its bed, the whole water seems alive, and is seen so black with fish, to a great distance, that the number seems inexhaustible. The herring were followed by massive cod, spurdog, tope and smooth-hound, longfin and bluefin tuna, blue, porbeagle, thresher, maiko and occasional great white sharks. Moving in behind within sight of the shore, were pods of fin whales and sperm whales.'

Oliver Goldsmith, novelist, playwright and encyclopaedist,

History of Earth and Animated Nature, 1776

THE ISLE OF MULL

How wild is the sea? I mean the sea off our shores today, the busy sea with fishing vessels, dredgers, tankers and container ships moving across it. The eruption of life that Oliver Goldsmith described in the eighteenth century reads, by contrast, like something made up, a fantasy. Yet just occasionally, we are privileged to catch a glimpse of what was once evidently commonplace. Spectacles such as those witnessed in Goldsmith's day do still occur from time to time, making his observations more believable, though they happen far less predictably and less often. One of these is what on the west coast of Scotland is known as a 'boiling', a brief period on the highest of spring tides when the birds and fish all seem to go crazy. I was privileged to see a boiling one summer when the mackerel shoals came into the bay where we stay on the Ross of Mull. Older locals said that they hadn't seen a boiling for years; most younger locals had never seen one.

People had said earlier in the week, as they do in late July or August, that the mackerel were 'in'. This usually means that if you go out in a boat or cast out a team of feathers or tinsel lures from the pier with a metal weight on the end, you will catch your supper. If you are lucky, you will catch several mackerel, which will be fairly deep in the water. Usually, you will not have seen them until they hook up. This time, while I was helping some young visitors to tackle up, I noticed black shoals of fry gathering around the pier. I thought nothing more of it until the next day, when there was an exceptionally high spring tide that came right up over the small area of salt marsh outside the village hostelry.

That evening, we looked out through the windows of the bar and wondered what was causing such a commotion on the surface of the water. We went outside and heard the sound of plopping. It was clear that the mackerel were not only 'in', they were right inshore, skimming the grassy foreshore a few inches beneath the surface, hunting in packs like little striped tigers and forcing the herring fry to hide in thickets of sedge. When the dark-backed herring fry's hiding places were discovered, they exploded in a flash of silver into the air and even up on to the turf to get away from their ravening predators. By picking up a few of these dying fugitives, I was able to identify that the fry were indeed juvenile herring.

We quickly went back home to get rods so that the novice anglers among us – yes, I'm an angler, too – could have a cast or two and so we could catch some supper. Our home is on the shore, further round the bay, and when we got there we were greeted by a sight we had never seen before in water that seldom reaches more than three metres deep even on a spring tide.

Rafts of ducks and geese were paddling about excitedly, seagulls were swooping and crying. Above them all were wheeling and diving gannets, rarely seen in the shallow part of the bay, plunging and picking off what looked like small baitfish, not the mackerel themselves. The fry were being forced up to the surface by these small cousins of big tuna. How the gannets managed to dive in the shallow water and not impale themselves in the bottom with their sharp beaks, was a wonder in itself.

Meanwhile, the tyro human fishers were taken to a suitable

vantage point and duly caught a mackerel with every cast on a small silver spinner. They came back home jubilant while I waited out this extraordinarily high tide in the encroaching gloom by the sea wall at the bottom of the garden. I was largely oblivious to the swarms of midges biting me as I watched the water boil and the marauding mackerel use the rest of the tide to finish their massacre of the juvenile herring in the tussocks of grass. By the next morning's high tide, the mackerel had returned to deep water as if nothing had happened but the little silver bodies of the herring fry that had jumped too far still lay scattered on the grass.

This spectacular feeding frenzy, right at my feet and involving so many creatures, made me wonder how wild the sea really is. Obviously, the ocean is a wilder place than a cultivated field. The assumption almost all of us naturally make is that the sea is a wild place, populated with wild animals and subject to wild events like the one I had just witnessed. We imagine that the few miles closest to the shore are the greatest altered extent by human influence, but to what degree? The close seas are less 'wild' than at some time in the past but how much less wild? In other words, how different is the sea off our shores from a wilderness or the unexploited state of Oliver Goldsmith's day, or long before that?

In the case of the mackerel, we know that the spawning population is in relatively good shape for reasons due more to nature than good management, and that there is an international fleet of huge midwater trawlers dedicated to catching it, not particularly well constrained by north-east Atlantic nations. In recent years, dissenting fishing nations such as Iceland, Russia and the Faroes have declared their own allowable catches, rather than subjecting themselves to the scientific consensus of the regional management organisation for the North East Atlantic Fisheries Commission, or the NEAFC. These northern nations claim that the mackerel has moved north thanks to their now warmer seas and their shares should increase accordingly, while the southern Europeans' shares should go down. This, of course, the Spanish, the Irish, the British and others refuse to accept. There is some truth in what the northerners say about how far north the mackerel now go but there is less justification for their failure to resort to their common treaty's dispute resolution mechanisms. They are risking the stock, which happens in fisheries management over and over again.

Consider, though, what has gone. The arrival of the herring schools in autumn on the north-east coast of the UK used to rank as one of the great spectacles of nature. The herring arrived in waves lapping down the east coast of Britain and provided an annual bonanza for fishermen and their families from Wick to Lowestoft. The herring schools came from many populations that spawned at different times and schools formed only when the herring were about to spawn. Fishermen in pursuit of herring would scan the horizon for the blow of whales, the leaping of fish pursued by predators beneath and the wheeling of birds.

The spectacle was immense, as were the economic benefits. In and around 1870, some 800,000 barrels of herring were cured in Scotland. Kippers – smoked herring – were the breakfast of choice in country houses and hotels up and down the kingdom. Over the following decades, the plenty ebbed away under fishing pressure. After the Second World War, there was a massive decrease in the spawning stock, largely caused by overfishing, followed by years of poor breeding success. Though fishing for herring was banned for a few years from 1977 in the hope of prompting recovery, this was arguably done too late and the herring has never fully returned to its former profusion (though there is an argument that this would still be possible if we protected its spawning grounds). The predators that used to follow the herring off the east coast are vastly diminished too, though fish-eating whales, now protected in UK waters, have been increasingly seen in the North Sea feasting off pulses of squid and no doubt some herring too.

The minke whale, a fish-eating whale sometimes seen off the mouth of our bay on the Isle of Mull, is still numerous, thanks to the global ban on whaling agreed in the 1980s – though minkes from the same population as those we see in the west of Scotland are sometimes killed by Norway and Iceland and, in Antarctic waters, by Japan. The minke's population is described as 'of least concern' by the International Union for the Conservation of Nature on its Red List, which in conservation passes for good news. The sharks, however, are in poor shape. Porbeagle, which once grew to half the size of a great white shark, is now listed as 'vulnerable' in UK seas. Tope is known to have declined by 88 per cent over the last 80 years and, as a result, has recently been reclassified from vulnerable to critically endangered. Spurdog – a predator of herring rather than mackerel – is also listed as vulnerable, as it reproduces slowly and matures late like all sharks. There is debate about whether great white sharks are found around the British coast at all. The poor shape the sharks are in and the fact that no one had seen a 'boiling' of mackerel such as the one we saw for many years give a very rough sense of how much has changed. Maybe 200 years ago there would have been sharks or tuna visible from the shore chasing the mackerel chasing the herring fry. There is none today.

Mackerel are one of the commercially fished north-east Atlantic stocks that are currently not overfished, according to the European Commission, though its opinion cannot always be relied on. That leaves 43 per cent of stocks in the North East Atlantic, including four out of five spawning stocks of cod, that are overfished. In the Mediterranean, a shocking 83 per cent of all fish stocks are currently overfished, despite a European law supposedly preventing that from happening. Overfishing is a definition of how fish are being exploited now and whether this allows reproduction at a rate which would allow stocks to grow. It does not consider how large the population once was before industrial exploitation or if it could recover to that level, which would be higher than it was even in, say, 1945. If we consider how much the populations of bottom-dwelling fish such as cod, haddock and halibut have reduced since the beginning of the industrial era, the losses are truly astonishing.

A study by Ruth Thurstan at the University of York[1] looked at the impact of 118 years of industrial fishing on UK bottom-trawl fisheries. She found that a trawl fleet in the 1880s, which consisted mostly of sailing boats open to the elements, was vastly more successful at catching fish than we are today. For every hour spent fishing today, in boats equipped with the most up-to-date technology, including fish-finders and other electronics, fishermen now land just 6 per cent of what they did 130 years ago. The simple reason for that stark contrast, concludes Professor Callum Roberts, a historian of overfishing, is that there are fewer fish in the sea. When the figures were broken down by type of fish, the contrast was even more extreme. Landings per unit of fishing power were down 36 times for plaice, 100 times for haddock and an astonishing 500 times for halibut, two-metre-plus giants of which were once regularly pulled from the waters of Dogger Bank and the Irish Sea.

The seas off our coasts are therefore an altered place – particularly when it comes to bottom-living and slow-growing fish. If our seas are still 'wild' places, where natural processes continue to work and remain productive, as I think they are, we have to accept that they are to an absolutely massive extent less productive than they were. So what *should* the seas be like, or what would their 'natural' state be, given that by most indications they are in decline, and that we have assumed responsibility to present and future generations to restore them? It is a hard question to answer after a millennia or more of fishing for bottom-living fish, such as cod in Europe, and with so few places where it is impossible for fishing vessels – and other industries such as gravel abstraction, oil and gas production and wind farms – to go. Are there, we should ask, any truly and origin-ally wild places left in the oceans of the world? And if so, can they show us what our seas ought to be?

I found an answer, of a kind, to that first question in a paper which said that some 13 per cent of the global ocean is wilderness and that this percentage is diminishing all the time.[2] The scientists who came up with that conclusion looked for biologically intact seascapes, that is wilderness, undisturbed by humans. They found what they defined as wilderness mostly in the high seas and in the Southern Ocean around Antarctica. They identified very little wil-derness in the northern hemisphere or in the tropics. They found only 4 per cent of what they called wilderness in marine protected areas – which is a challenge for the world's conservation community. But looking at the maps or charts of what this particular group of scientists considered wilderness, one has to observe that there is quite a difference between some areas and others. Some of the areas listed as wilderness had been quite heavily exploited in the past, for example by whalers and sealers in the Southern Ocean and the Pacific in historical times – meaning they had been stripped of megafauna, such as the great whales. Some of the tropical areas they identified as wilderness were once fished by fishermen who simply aren't there any more as the areas were depopulated (such as the Chagos archipelago in the Indian Ocean, where the human population was removed). So, if you define wilderness as unaffected by human use in the past, there is some doubt about whether 'true' wilderness actually amounts to 13 per cent of the ocean after all.

Some areas they described look like near pristine wilderness but when you look closely and factor in what you know about the historic uses of those parts of the ocean, some of these places are in reality restored wilderness. They have been rewilded. This fits with what we know: the ocean is more dynamic than the land and very few creatures actually go completely extinct, so wilderness in the ocean may not be a finite and eroding commodity but a fluctuating one. It may be that we can actually recreate wildness, or wilderness, by removing human influences. According to this alternative point of view, wilderness is not a fast-eroding bastion of something absolute that used to exist; it is dynamic, evolving.

Thinking of wilderness in a way that actually takes account of how the ocean's creatures have reacted to events in geological time means that rather than wringing our hands and bemoaning the lost wilderness that once spanned the Earth, we can try to bring something else back. If we are not returning the ocean to its original state, then we can allow it to reach a new wild equilibrium. Nature never stands still – as one can see around the coasts from colonists such as the little egret, the red mullet or the anchovy, that just turn up in places they never lived before. If nature is left alone, it is capable of recreating the pristine. And if we can recreate the pristine, by unlocking the power of nature, why can't we do that much closer to where most people live, as others have done on land by turning farmland back to wild land and by introducing keystone species such as wolves, wild boar, wild cattle and beavers?

The idea of 'rewilding' was coined about the land many decades before people began to use it about the sea, as indeed we were among the first to do. The term is used in both contexts by people who have been exasperated by the failings of conventional conservation wisdom. Instead of focusing on managing a feature, like a reef, or a species, such as salmon, rewilding tries to restore whole ecosystems. It was only when I began reading the exploits of rewilders on land that I realised how similar their work was to what the leading advocates of marine protected areas, such as the late New Zealander Bill Ballantine, had been saying since the 1970s about the sea. Ballantine was a passionate advocate of stepping back and letting natural processes restore the sea, any bit of sea, because nature knew far better how to do this than us and would do it in unexpected ways. Conventional wisdom is wary of allowing nature anywhere near the driving seat. Ballantine was all for it.

The idea of rewilding, of stepping back and letting nature take control, remains controversial among the high priests of official nature conservation in government agencies and academic institutions. Officialdom prefers to believe in the serene scientific management of nature by us – which assumes that humans are god-like creatures, devoid of base instincts, who actually know what we are doing. The reality is that we humans are fallible, don't know everything and are politically influenced, by economic factors and by dogma, and it can take generations to correct our mistakes. The saying goes that science advances one funeral at a time as the deaths of fierce advocates of past orthodoxy allow newer ideas to gain ground. Yet it doesn't take much study to grasp the reality that most forms of marine management, whether of fish stocks or areas set aside for nature conservation, are failing because they don't control all destructive influences.

What ecologists on land or sea spend most of their time doing, therefore, is monitoring decline. Ballantine said that instead of placing our faith in the 'experts' to choose marine protected area networks of ecologically representative features, we should just protect anywhere at all in the sea and it would actually become interesting. Nature, uninfluenced by man, would make it so. He was convinced of it, but other than in his own local reserve he didn't get many other opportunities to try it out. Official nature conservation in New Zealand is as obsessed with evidence-based selection of sites, on the basis of habitats and features, as it is everywhere else.

I went to see Bill not far from the shores of the world's oldest no-take marine reserve at Goat Island, 50 miles north of Auckland, New Zealand. There he pointed out changes that no scientist predicted until the University of Auckland was persuaded to create a no-take reserve – just to see what would happen. At the time it was protected in 1975, entirely for the purposes of scientific research, the seabed at Goat Island was known as rock barrens. By the 2000s, the snapper had grown to prodigious size. They had eaten the sea urchins, which in the past had eaten all the kelp and prevented it from returning. What had been an area of bare rock had been transformed into a kelp forest, populated by unfrightened and curious fish the size of small pigs. This was my first encounter with a top-down 'trophic cascade' – where the survival or reintroduction of one or two species alters an entire ecosystem, creating a different balance and greater diversity.

The story of rewilding on land is full of such unexpected occurrences. One of the most documented trophic cascades is the return of wolves to Yellowstone in 1995, a change likened by Doug Smith, a wildlife biologist in charge of the project, to kicking a pebble down a mountain slope when conditions are just right to trigger an avalanche. The removal of wolves in the 1930s had changed the behaviour of the elk, which browsed the stands of willow along the streams. This was tough on beavers which need willow bark to survive in the winter. The reintroduction of wolves meant the elk moved on more often and broke up into smaller units, leading to the regrowth of willow, which led in turn to an increase in the number of beavers. The beavers dammed the rivers which started to hold their course and so less erosion was evident.

Some saw the introduction of wolves as responsible for changing rivers and fixing a broken Yellowstone; others saw a more complex picture in which wolves, operating in concert with other large carnivores, such as the bear and cougar, improved the health of the streams. People love arguing about large carnivores and what part they play, and how many domestic livestock they kill, but undoubtedly the wolves do seem to have caused a trophic cascade. The wolf-killed carcasses benefit a whole web of life from beetles and wolverines to lynx and ravens. Native American legends of ravens following wolves turned out to be true. Wolves mean food for multiple forms of life, which ravens knew.

The return of the wolf is not just a New World phenomenon. Wolves are recolonising the east of Germany and the Italian and French Alps. Wilderness is returning to all sorts of places which once used to be farmed and where the offspring of the former human inhabitants have departed to the cities. This movement of wildlife was accelerated by populations of wolves, brown bear and boar fleeing northwards during the Balkan wars.

One of the most controversial examples of rewilding in Europe is the Oostvaardersplassen. There, half an hour's drive from Amsterdam, bounded on one side by a major road along a dyke, lies a 23-square-mile (6,000-hectare) land reclamation project that did not go to plan. It is part of a polder – land reclaimed from the sea – called South Flevoland. It was made with some 166 square miles (43,00 hectares) of land reclaimed from the IJsselmeer, Lake IJssel in English, a huge, closed-off freshwater lake that once formed part of the salt-water bay, the Zuiderzee, or South Sea. Thanks to a delay in planned land reclamation schemes – put on hold by the oil crisis of the early 1970s – the Oostvaardersplassen never fully dried out. Marsh vegetation developed around the pools. It was discovered by migrating birds. Since 1986, it has been an officially designated nature reserve. By the time I visited in the 1990s, there were spoon-bills wading in the shallows, white-tailed eagles feuding with marsh harriers and bitterns booming in the reedbeds. It now has some 250 bird species, all of which just rolled up.

Most numerous of these arrivistes were greylag geese, 30,000 of them, almost half the population of north-west Europe in one relatively small area. The greylags taught the ecologists something they were not expecting. Grazing over the period of the summer moult, while they waited for their flight feathers to grow again, the geese ate a vast amount of marsh vegetation and prevented the ponds from closing over with reeds and trees from growing on the banks and in the grassland. All this unexpected activity challenged prevailing theories of how land evolved and became covered with canopied forests without humans.

As the Dutch ecologist Frans Vera put it: 'This was the astonishing thing: the geese were leading vegetarian succession – not the other way round. But more than that their grazing was adding to biodiversity. The geese were changing extensive reed beds into a more complex habitat of reeds and shallow water, and this was attracting more species than other wetland reserves in the Netherlands that were carefully managed by humans.'

The controversial bit was to come. Grazing animals, such as deer, wild cattle and ponies, were introduced to keep the grazing meadows open for the geese, as the geese were now recognised as a keystone species – i.e. one that helps define an ecosystem. But the Oostvaardersplassen was not large enough for the herds to migrate somewhere else when the grass failed and they grew hungry. In winter, when the grass died back, many animals starved. The annual die-off was something the public found distressing – though starvation is a fundamental factor of nature. Now, as a compromise, animals that cannot be supported by the limited grazing are humanely culled. The influence of large browsing and grazing animals on the vegetation is to turn a piece of reclaimed land into one of the closest things one will ever see to what wilderness looked like on the European continent at the beginning of the current geological epoch, the Holocene, about 11,650 years ago.

An equally inspiring example of rewilding on land that was, on paper, of little conservation importance at the outset is the Knepp Castle Estate, some 3,500 acres just south of Horsham in Sussex. There, a sizeable holding of English farmland only 44 miles from central London has been transformed into a pioneering rewilding experiment, the first of its kind in Britain. The dairy farms on heavy Sussex clay that Sir Charles Burrell inherited from his parents were failing and needed millions of pounds of investment if they were to continue on the path of intensive agriculture – but he worked out that the proceeds were unlikely to keep the farms in profit. A 'moment of epiphany' came in 2002, when Charlie and his wife Isabella Tree received Countryside Stewardship funding to restore 350 acres of parkland designed by Sir Humphry Repton (a disciple of Capability Brown) at the heart of the estate, which had been under the plough since the Second World War. That led the Burrells to look at the land in a different way and suggested the possibility of taking down the fences and rolling out nature conservation across the whole estate. In an extraordinarily short space of time, the land has been transformed into looking like 'the Maasai Mara, or the Okavango Delta in Africa' – in Isabella's own words from her bestselling book, *Wilding: The Return of Nature to an English Farm.*

In the now-overgrown hedgerows in June comes the purring of turtle doves, one of Britain's fastest declining birds; Knepp has become one of their last strongholds. Also present are other rare species, such as nightingale, peregrine falcons and purple emperor butterflies, not found on neighbouring farmland. Knepp makes its income now from wildlife safaris – for which there is growing demand – as well as glamping, wild-grown meat and property letting. All of this would not be possible if the estate were not in receipt of the top tier of government subsidies for nature conservation, for which after a long struggle Isabella and Charlie managed to qualify. And why not? It is far and away more successful at attracting wildlife than most statutory protected areas. Knepp's safaris to see nightingales, kingfishers, bats and moths, owls and bees are fully booked from summer to autumn. Knepp is shaping the future of nature conservation and of experiencing the countryside. As the distinguished ecologist Professor Sir John Lawton put it: 'If we can bring back nature at this scale and pace just 16 miles from Gatwick airport we can do it anywhere. I have seen it. It's truly wonderful and it fills me with hope.'

Is it fanciful to think that these beacons of hope on land have a message for rewilding the sea? Or that we might one day rewild the more heavily used parts of it, those closest to our shores, as we have some of the most heavily worked bits of land? Not at all. On land, rewilded areas are a challenge to the way we have gone about conservation over the last century or so in Europe, attempting to protect and manage fragmented species and habitats that have somehow survived, rather than recreating the ecosystems of which they were once part. That approach of managing features makes even less sense in the sea, which is more three dimensional, free-flowing, dynamic and much harder to control. The decision to protect features seems to have been adopted because establishment conservationists didn't know what else to do when they were asked to protect the biodiversity of the sea – despite being told exactly what to do by Ballantine and his followers on numerous occasions. So in Europe, we have ended up with a network of marine protected areas – 'marine reserves' would mean something much more protected than what we have – that attempts to protect what lives on the bottom but perversely not what swims and migrates through the water column, though it does often relate to what flies through the air. The species in the water column, the fish, are managed by fisheries scientists, working under fisheries ministries and under different treaties. Though the protection of functioning ecosystems is supposedly an aspiration of official policy, it is being done with two competing intellectual systems in one place, one with more of a commercial bias than the other. The runaway successes of rewilding on land – as well as one or two international examples of rewilding in the sea – provide a strong case that we should try a 'whole site' approach in the sea, protecting everything from the top to the bottom of the water column, to get the best from any area we decide needs protecting.

The terrestrial examples do make an overwhelming case for the setting-aside of places in the sea where nature can be left 'in the driving seat' and where we can see what happens without any human influences at all. For the health of the oceans, these should be as large as possible and that there should be many of them. But it is important to remember that bringing our oceans back to health depends on other things too, on the treaties that govern species such as whales and bluefin tuna that migrate across whole oceans and, inevitably, in and out of protected areas. The numbers of large highly migratory creatures cannot be subjected to uncontrolled attrition if the ocean is to be truly wild.

Then we come to the biggest question of all: how should we deal with the places where there will inevitably always be human influences? The oceans are the last place where modern society depends largely on hunter gatherers; here, fishers depend for their living on catching wild animals. If we are to have healthy seas, can we abandon those areas of the sea that are fished, and which are likely always to be fished, to the processes described as 'fishing down the food web', the relentless simplification which comes with fishing out the large fish, then the medium-sized species and ultimately being reduced to catching shellfish when the fish are gone? To my mind, it would be irresponsible to do nothing to build back the web of life in those places where fishing techniques have destroyed the largest creatures and relentlessly simplified complex and biodiverse marine ecosystems – the Firth of Clyde in Scotland is but one of many examples. In the best-managed of areas, the protection of biodiversity can co-exist with earning a living and feeding a family, and fishermen can become – if they are not already – custodians of the sea. If we want to enlist the full range of support from those users of the sea who wish to see it managed responsibly and to restore the plenty that it once had, it seems axiomatic to me that we should set our definition of rewilding as wide as possible and be considerate to all the users of the sea with good intentions, or we will end up like a bunch of greens sitting in the corner of a bar talking to themselves. If we are to rewild the sea for the good of all, then we should involve as many people as possible in this great and worthwhile adventure.

2

If In Doubt, Think Big

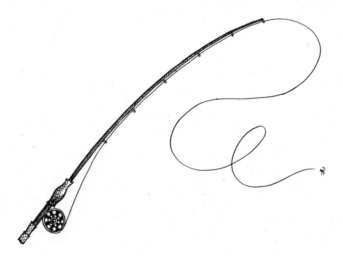

'*Rivers and the inhabitants of the watery elements are meant for wise men to contemplate and for fools to pass by without consideration.*'

Izaak Walton, *The Compleat Angler*, 1653

I had many adventures in my three decades in journalism but at no point did it occur to me that one day I would find myself, with my friends, in the position to help create the world's largest marine reserve – in a place we had never visited, with over 220 species of coral and more than 800 species of fish, in the middle of the Indian Ocean. By the time that fleeting opportunity came into view, and we grasped it, I had become a supporter of a big idea. In order to protect our seas back home, we needed to protect the last wildernesses of the sea across the globe and restore them to fecundity, both for their own sake and to show people how much richer they were than what was left off our shores.

My own path to the ocean ran down rivers, through reservoirs and across lochs, and ultimately along that subterranean tributary of the River Thames, the River Fleet, in the last days when Fleet Street was a place where journalists at all levels worked and socialised together. My passion as a child and as a teenager was catching trout on a fly, though I have no objection to catching pike, eels, carp, bass, pollack and mackerel by other means. Rivers, reservoirs, lochs and studying and imitating their fly life through manuals on entomology were my introduction to ecology.

I was a country boy sent to a central London boarding school to escape the decline of the family milling business. After a degree in English and Philosophy at the University of York, I came to the *Daily Telegraph* in 1981 via a brief job on the *Spectator*, working for its editor, Alexander Chancellor, whom I revered. He passed me on to the *Telegraph*, where something in my rural background, as the son of a farmer and miller and a horsewoman turned Spitfire pilot and organic farmer, appealed to the *Daily Telegraph*'s editor, W. F. Deedes. Bill was a household name as 'Dear Bill', the recipient of the fictional letters of Denis Thatcher in *Private Eye*, a column which described the Thatcher era from a mixture of leaks and inspired imaginings. Bill was approachable but mercurial. He did not often talk about himself. I learned many years later, from a member of his family, that Bill hired me because I embodied a strand of his own rural past that he wanted to see represented in the paper alongside the confident outpourings of the bright young Oxbridge-educated ideologues and put-out-to-pasture old reporters who usually inhabited the comment and diary columns he presided over.

Deedes's editorial conferences were a rapid initiation into high politics, interrupted as they occasionally were at times of crisis by phone calls from members of the Thatcher circle. But I struggled to find a useful role on the paper, other than as a sub-editor, so I wrote for magazines like the *Field* and *Country Life* in my spare time. That all changed when Deedes was succeeded by another editor, Max Hastings, who was not only a fly fisherman like me and had read my stuff in the *Field* but who had a thorough understanding of environmental issues.

Hastings was hired by a new management at the *Telegraph* to modernise the paper for a younger readership. To do so, he decided he needed to keep abreast of the wave of environmental concern that erupted after the disasters of Chernobyl and Bhopal in the mid-1980s, alongside growing anxieties about the thinning stratospheric ozone layer, shortly to be followed by climate change. He hired me as environment correspondent. The *Telegraph*'s style was fact-filled, unflowery and it told things how they were without technicalities, so environmental concepts required some deft explaining. The paper's large readership at that time included matter-of-fact but knowledgeable folk in business, farming and the services who could nevertheless quickly become emotional about country matters, about the decline of butterflies or wild-flower meadows.

Everything one wrote about the countryside, then, lay under the shadow of the brutally honest report by the Nature Conservancy Council, about the damage caused to the British landscape since 1945 by subsidised agriculture and forestry. Its authors recorded a great roll-call of damage that I can still reel off in my sleep. Since the Second World War, Great Britain had lost 95 per cent of its wildflower-rich hay meadows; 80 per cent of its limestone grass-land; 40 per cent of its lowland heaths; 30–50 per cent of its ancient and semi-natural lowland woods and 150,000 miles of hedges. The toll of devastation kept mounting because of the EU subsidies for intensive farming described memorably at the time by the environment minister, William Waldegrave, as 'the engine of destruction'. The effect of subsidies is pretty similar in the sea.

By the early nineties, when I wrote a book with the Prince of Wales about his attempt to restore some of that damage to the countryside through his experiments in organic farming at High-grove, another 63,000 miles of hedgerow had gone. Green farming schemes came and went. Individual farmers who cared did what they could. The Prince of Wales's experiments in organic farming were, I believe, part of a desire to go one better than that and find a way to put back what was lost into the farming regime. Rewilding was not a word he used at the time but arguably he was one of its first exponents on land, trying to co-exist with skylarks, grey partridges and wildflowers in the crops themselves, rather than banishing them to the margins. That aspiration to put back what has been lost is only now finding its way to the oceans.

When I became an environment correspondent I found, to my delight, that the job also meant reporting about the state of rivers, waterways and the sea. My first Hastings-inspired campaign was against the impact of conifer forestry – railed against by the NCC in its famous 1984 report. It turned out that the dark, subsidised spruce blankets being planted in the uplands not only displaced moorland birds and dried up bogs, but also soaked up sulphur emissions from coal-fired power stations and leached acid into rivers. This had disastrous results for catchments which were already on the margins of acidity, taking pH levels over a threshold that salmon and sea trout could not survive. By writing about a succession of celebrities – Terry Wogan and Cliff Richard among them – who enjoyed tax breaks by investing in conifers, the *Daily Telegraph* persuaded the chancellor of the day, Nigel Lawson, to abolish tax breaks for forestry altogether so the planting of conifer blankets in wild places was halted.

The preoccupation of environmental groups when I took on this field in the late 1980s was with pollution – understandably, in the decade of Chernobyl and acid rain. The growing evidence of overfishing was studiously ignored. The disagreeable practice of dumping treated sewage sludge into the Thames estuary released heavy metals and Greenpeace published pictures of flatfish with deformities that may – or may not – have been caused by these. A few of us noted that these sub-lethal effects were inconsequential in contrast to the lethal effect upon millions of wild animals caused by the nation's commercial fishing industry.

One of the reports which crossed my desk at the time that made a lasting impression was about the challenges faced by the salmon of the River Wye on the border of England and Wales. Its author, David Solomons, concluded that the main reason for the disappearance of the great Wye strain of salmon, which in the years after the war used to run to more than 40lbs in weight, was not netting at sea, or disease, or acid rain, as everyone then thought, but overfishing by anglers with rod and line. If anglers could be responsible for overfishing a migratory species with flies and spinners, I asked myself, what on earth were trawling and other industrial methods capable of doing to fish in the sea?

Over the next decade or so, I began to realise that the impact of human activity on the oceans was a rich seam, journalistically speaking. Perhaps it helped that my colleagues on *The Times* or the *Guardian* would usually get the latest ground-breaking story about climate change on the front page whereas, however well I wrote it, the right-of-centre, disinclined-to-panic *Daily Telegraph* would make it a nice big page lead with a picture on page eight. The oceans, the planet's largest commons, were less of an ideological battleground and writing about them was a less crowded field, where stories found their way on to the front page on merit.

That is not to say we did not cover climate change; indeed, we covered one of the most important stories of the time more prominently than anyone else. I got word, the day before, of Margaret

Thatcher's 1988 speech to the Royal Society about climate change in which she was to say that, 'We have unwittingly begun a massive experiment with the system of the planet itself.' My colleague in the parliamentary lobby Philip Johnston duly wrote it up the next day. His first version was influenced by his colleagues among the jaundiced lobby correspondents who weren't much interested in science and saw this flash of greenery by Mrs T in political terms – as a response to the Greens winning a record vote in the European elections or an attempt to steal votes from the Lib Dems.

I rang Phil when I saw his copy arrive and told him how important I knew certain confidential contacts of mine thought this speech was. It not only marked the raising of the climate change debate to the level at which other world leaders would have to respond but it also marked a watershed after which all sorts of government policies would have to change. Phil instantly registered that we were sitting on a better story than the rest of the lobby realised it was. He generously agreed that we would rewrite it together, then persuaded the *Telegraph* to make it the front-page lead, the 'splash'. The *Telegraph* was the only national paper to do so.

The atmospheric science bandwagon had begun to roll and public awareness of climate change was increasing, but even then it was noticeable that the other global commons, the ocean, was not getting much attention. I remember sitting around with a few other correspondents at one of the proliferating number of climate change events with a mentor of ours, Dr David Fisk, then chief scientist to the UK Department of the Environment. He told us: 'If you think these figures coming through on climate change look bad, you should look at some of the data coming across my desk on fisheries' – that is, on overfishing. This was a year or so before anyone knew about the collapse of the northern cod stocks on the Grand Banks off Newfoundland, the story that was to cast a shadow over ocean science and politics for a decade. A moratorium on cod fishing on the Grand Banks was declared by Canadian federal Minister of Fisheries and Oceans John Crosbie in 1992. The disaster ended a way of life of catching, salting and selling cod that had existed for around 500 years. It was caused by mismanagement based on a culture of highly politicised scientific decision-making. A priestly caste deluded themselves that cod were there in large numbers and excluded the views of those independent minds, such as the late Professor R.A.M. Myers, who said they were declining fast. The cod still struggle to return decades later.

I am getting ahead of myself, for there were inklings on the eastern side of the Atlantic, too, of the immense destructiveness of fishing with modern technology. At a conference in the Hague in 1990, I saw an artist's impression of what trawling with a beam trawl does to the bottom of the North Sea. The gist of the paper by Han Lindeboom of the Texel Institute was that there were parts of the sea which were trawled seven times a year with enormous destructive impact not only on fish but upon the organisms that lived on the seabed. As a farmer's son, I knew that on land not much would grow under those circumstances. Beam trawling with 'tickler chains' that stirred flatfish off the bottom into the trawl net caught fish more efficiently than any other method. The flailing caused by the chains actually made the seabed more productive for a short time for the trawlermen because fish flooded in to prey on the smashed shellfish and other marine organisms that were left behind. But constant trawling ultimately left the ecosystem simplified or just barren.

Something else I discovered was the disgraceful part played by the Danish sand-eel fleet in undermining the whole North Sea ecosystem. It was catching so many of these small, short-lived fish that fishmeal factories were selling the oil to power stations to aid the combustion of low-grade, sulphurous coal. To me, selling animal oil as fuel was as much of an obscenity with fish as it was with whales. No one seemed to care that the removal of small fish at the bottom of the food chain appeared also to be preventing the regeneration of cod, causing the breeding failure of seabirds, such as arctic terns and puffins, and contributing to the decline of salmon, sea trout and other fish.

Shortly after I exposed the practice of burning sand-eel oil, the stock simply collapsed. It has been argued that expecting to catch large, palatable fish, such as cod, and small fish that they feed on, such as capelin or sand eel, from the same ocean is simply incompatible and should not happen together in the same place if either population or the ecosystem are to thrive. But the sand eels eventually recovered to a lesser extent, after fishing was banned for a few years, and the Danish fleet goes on fishing on Dogger Bank with its small-mesh nets.

The late 1990s were a time when, partly thanks to the dawning understanding of what caused the disaster on the Grand Banks, conservation measures began to bite on a North Sea fishing fleet that was vastly over-large compared to the stocks of fish that were left to catch. Instead of tying up the fleet and keeping to the quotas, cheating began. A succession of small east-coast ports was engaged in the landing of 'black fish'. Fish was being landed in the dead of night and trucked straight to processing factories. Landings data were being falsified all over the country. My sources told me that every other cod caught in the North Sea was being landed illegally – a figure later officially confirmed by the European Union's fisheries inspectorate.[1] It was a scandal that led the front page just after the 1997 general election.

Wherever you looked around the world in the 1990s and early 2000s there were stories of disaster caused by too much fishing technology, but the official annual catch records compiled by the UN Food and Agriculture Organisation kept going up. This mystery was solved by Daniel Pauly who analysed the official statistics and found that the numbers submitted by China were just made up (by Communist party officials who only won preferment if the figures increased) and that the world's catches of wild fish had been in decline since around 1996.[2] A limit to growth had been reached and the world had not even known it at the time. Overfishing was, overnight, understood as a global problem.

A literary agent, Ivan Mulcahy, rang me in 2002, the same year as Pauly's letter was published in *Nature*, and said he was looking for a book on the subject of overfishing. He'd heard from a friend that I'd already written it. I had been trying to interest publishers in such a book since 1997, so far without success, but I would happily try again. I got started on a synopsis of what became *The End of the Line: How Overfishing is Changing the World and What We Eat*.

To illustrate the unseen impacts of trawling to the general reader, I decided to imagine what it would be like if huge machines dragged a beam trawl across the savannahs of Africa. These contraptions would scoop up everything in their way: predators, such as lions and cheetahs, lumbering herbivores, such as rhinos and elephants, herds of impalas and wildebeest, family groups of warthog and wild dog. At the same time, the rolling beam would smash and flatten obstructions, flushing creatures into the approaching filaments, leaving behind a bedraggled landscape resembling a harrowed field. I explained that this was what trawling did to the world's oceans every day.

My book was well reviewed but nothing much appeared to change in the world of public policy. This was disappointing and I made the discovery that change was what I was seeking. The answer, I decided, was to get the message out to a larger audience. There began a two-year search for a way of putting the book on the big screen. I teamed up with two seasoned producers, Claire Lewis and Christopher Hird. They thought we should make an independent documentary feature on the lines of Al Gore's *An Inconvenient Truth*. If in doubt, think big. Fortunately, Christo brought in George Duffield, who unlocked the funding to make this a global story. We were pestered by a film director, Rupert Murray, who had picked up my book at an airport and was unable to put it down. We decided to give Rupert a crack at directing the film as he was talented and cared about the subject.

Rupert chose to focus on one of the stories in the book, the critically endangered bluefin, as he saw it as the 'poster child' for the depletion of the ocean. His film sequences of the tuna slaughter in the Almadraba, the tuna traps in the Strait of Gibraltar, were extraordinarily powerful. Men gaffed enormous fish in a sea dyed red with blood. Elsewhere in the Mediterranean, fishing methods were more industrial – and almost entirely illegal. The use of spotter planes to track the tuna shoals aggregating to spawn was supposed to be banned in the Mediterranean in the month of June, yet a Greenpeace vessel photographed 11 such aircraft working with tuna vessels. A former fish-farm diver, Roberto Mielgo Bragazzi, now an investigator and one of the heroes of the film, flew to the airstrip on the Italian island of Lampedusa and managed to photograph the flight manifests: he said that the spotter planes were all retained by tuna fishing associations, mainly based in Naples with, he suspected, mafia links.

Bluefin were on the menu everywhere in Europe at that time; fashionistas and film stars flocked to London and New York branches of Nobu and other high-end restaurants to eat it. It was even available at a restaurant near where we filmed fishing ministers meeting in Luxembourg to discuss the bluefin's fate. The recommendation of the scientists of ICCAT, the Atlantic regional fisheries management organisation, was that catches should be limited to 15,000 tonnes so the bluefin could recover, but the members of the organisation set the quotas at 22,000 tons. Owing to rampant illegality, a fishing season that was far too long and non-observance of what rules there were, the total catch reached 61,000 tonnes in 2007. An internal review of ICCAT staffed with independent fisheries scientists described the management of the bluefin tuna as 'an international disgrace'. WWF predicted there would be no more adult bluefin capable of spawning by 2012 if things went on as they were.

Our film had its premiere in January 2009 at the Sundance Film Festival and in London that June. The film got noticed, thanks to

Greta Scacchi, siren of many Hollywood films, who volunteered to pose naked hugging a huge cod to promote the film and the concept that we needed to love and care more about fish, not just fluffy animals.* That memorable picture got the film talked about in the *Daily Mail* and then other papers. The film was also, more importantly, a critical success. As we discovered in Sundance and at its multi-cinema premiere in London, it made an unpredictably huge impression on live audiences. They asked us two questions, in some form, almost everywhere it was shown: why did nobody tell us that overfishing was a problem this big? And, what are you going to do to tackle this problem which nobody seems to be doing enough about? Retailers gave into our film's demands that the tuna they sold should be from responsibly managed fisheries. People wrote to us and asked us to support their campaigns. We showed the film in numerous countries and at the UN General Assembly in New York. It was translated into many languages. A study of the impact of the film by the Channel 4 Britdoc fund found that, in the UK, it had impacted more people than Al Gore's *An Inconvenient Truth*.

Then something rather extraordinary happened. All over Europe, the public seemed to notice the scandal of the critically endangered bluefin being overfished. The idea of serving fish as endangered as a rhino or a giant panda became unfashionable, as a result of people watching the film and word of mouth. Our film became a showreel for the campaign to save the bluefin. WWF Mediterranean decided that it was still getting nowhere with trying

---

* The first of a series that would become known as 'Fishlove', curated by Nicholas Röhl.

to get the fishing nations to manage tuna according to scientific advice. The conservation movement decided to go for a listing of the bluefin under the Convention on International Trade in Endangered Species – which would take the control of the bluefin trade away from fishing bodies altogether. The campaign was taken on by the little principality of Monaco which took on the EU and Japan in a David-versus-Goliath struggle. To the surprise of Brussels insiders, the campaign to list the bluefin under CITES progressed slowly through all the institutions of the European Union (with the help of more than one sympathetic British minister who made it government policy).

However, the campaign to CITES-list the bluefin did not succeed. Japan did not want international trade in bluefin to be regulated by a conservation treaty and it had nine months to gather its allies around it. That was a long time to prepare and it did the job well. The EU had two weeks and was in disarray. At a banquet held the night before the vote at the CITES meeting in Doha, Qatar, the Japanese delegation served bluefin to its cronies – a gesture of defiance by the fishing industry. The vote next day was lost – but the battle was won because on the way through Europe's institutions the decision had already been taken to manage the bluefin more strictly according to scientific advice. This agreement had the backing of Japan. These were the major players, so opposition in ICCAT crumbled. A new European commissioner, Maria Damanaki, enforced the scientific advice and slashed the fishing season in the Mediterranean, leading to the recovery we see today.

As I sat in Doha knocking out my copy for the *Sunday Times* about the bluefin vote, there came a flurry of emails from George

Duffield asking me to join him in starting a new marine conservation charity with Chris Gorell Barnes, the digital entrepreneur who, as an executive producer, had been key to promoting the film. I knew they wanted to act on the momentum of the film and set up a charity to create marine reserves, one of the things our film called for.[3] Would I join them? I hesitated – would I be able to pay the mortgage? – then took the plunge.

It seems odd now that we were not daunted by taking on established NGOs and foundations. For some reason, at the height of our film's success and with the campaign for the bluefin effectively won, it didn't bother us at all. Nobody else on our side of the Atlantic seemed to have our exclusive focus on tackling overfishing and creating marine reserves – so there was a niche to be filled. We drew confidence from our media experiences that some new campaign would come along and that we would be faster off the mark in reacting to it than the lumbering giants of conservation.

It did. And we were.

That 'big idea' was the subject of a consultation announced by the UK Foreign and Commonwealth Office in November 2009 on a proposed marine reserve, the largest in the world, around the Chagos Archipelago in the middle of the Indian Ocean. This remote tropical semi-paradise was a place so wild, we heard, that reef fish would swim towards humans out of curiosity rather than swimming away.

The archipelago consists of five atolls, including the Great Chagos Bank, the largest coral atoll in the world. Its unique habitats include 25,000 square miles of shallow reefs, enormous deep-sea plains, limestone platforms, 86 seamounts and 243 deep-sea knolls.

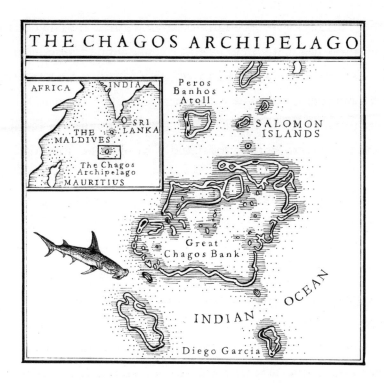

THE CHAGOS ARCHIPELAGO

The islands are surrounded by a kaleidoscope of life – 220 species of coral, 355 species of molluscs and 800 species of fish, including vast manta rays and more than 50 different types of shark. Above the surface, the islands are a breeding ground for seabirds as well as turtles and coconut crabs. If there was anywhere on Earth that was worth protecting, not just for itself but for its ability to preserve the biodiversity of a whole ocean, it was the Chagos Archipelago.

The enterprise was not without controversy. For the entire human population of the Chagos had been evicted from the territory by 1973, never to be allowed back. This was the result of a secret deal Britain concluded with the Pentagon in December 1966 to set up a huge US military base on Diego Garcia, the largest island.

Neither Parliament nor Congress were fully informed.[4] The fateful decision was taken, a Foreign Office memo later admitted, 'without adequate grasp of the character of the individual Chagos islands and the numbers of people inhabiting them.'

The forcible deportation of the Chagos's inhabitants was a brutal decision taken during the Cold War. It was apparently the consequence of a 1960 UN resolution on the right of self-determination. Britain realised it could only establish a new colony, the British Indian Ocean Territory, if no one lived there. When, in 1973, the entire Franco-Creole population of the territory on all the inhabited islands was expelled, their dogs gassed before the people were embarked, the British government asserted that the inhabitants of the islands were contract workers belonging to Mauritius or the Seychelles. This was not strictly true. As the British administrator recorded at the time, hundreds of them saw themselves as the Ilois, part of a coconut plantation society that had been brought over from Africa by the French, their first colonial masters, and which developed over 150 years, since 1814, under British rule. (The term Chagossian only began to be used in the 1990s.) The separation of the 'oil islands' from Mauritius, as that country became independent, was opposed by Mauritius's leadership at the time and has been challenged ever since. A minister told Parliament in the 1960s that Britain would return the islands to Mauritius when they were no longer required for defensive purposes. Forty years later, and after 9/11 and the invasions of Afghanistan and Iraq, little had changed: the UK and the US insisted their defence needs had not gone away. Except for Diego Garcia, the 58 islets of the archipelago had been abandoned to nature. Most of the former man-made structures had collapsed and the plantation areas had been over-taken by undergrowth.

The political realities being what they were, it seemed anom-alous to conservationists and scientists that Chagos's waters – one of the most pristine tropical marine environments on Earth – continued to be fished commercially, both for reef fish and for tuna (with a considerable bycatch of sharks and other species). The case for a large-scale marine protected area was put forward by a consortium of conservation organisations in 2009 and the British government announced a consultation on a marine protected area the same year, to which 250,000 people responded, 90 per cent of them in favour. Conservationists took trouble to make clear at the time that they did not see their support for a marine protected area as in any way in conflict with the human rights of the Chagossians and that if the Chagossians were one day allowed to recolonise their birthplace – which I for one strongly favoured – or Mauritius prevailed in its claim to sovereignty, all options might have to go back on the table. (It is perfectly possible to imagine artisanal and subsistence fishing zones around some of the larger, inhabit-able islands, as has been created around Diego Garcia, within the reserve and indeed this is what Chagossian groups argued for at the time of the consultation.)

Chagos was a big conservation prize. Declaring a 'no-take' reserve in the 640,000 sq kms of Chagos waters would double the global no-take area – then under 1 per cent of the whole – and protect 1.5 per cent of the world's near-surface coral reefs. At the time, the UK and the US governments were not going to budge on their decision on the occupation of the islands or allow the

Chagossians to re-settle any time soon, so conservationists decided to go with the art of the possible.

Soon, however, there was another problem: money. On the November day I was invited to a reception organised by the Chagos Conservation Trust to campaign for the no-take reserve, *The Times* reported that the permanent secretaries across government had met and curtailed any further expenditure that was in excess of its current commitments before the next election. It was just a year since the global financial crisis of 2008. Gordon Brown's Labour government was broke. The civil service had a duty to protect the next government from acts of profligacy. Across the room, my eyes met those of Alistair Gammell, who worked for the Pew Environment Group, one of the coalition of groups arguing for a reserve. I asked whether the coalition had made any plans to raise the extra money that would be needed to patrol the area once the sale of fishing licences to foreign tuna fleets to fish in Chagos's offshore waters ceased. I gathered the coalition of conservationists had been expecting the Foreign Office to pay for it. At that moment we both realised that the story in *The Times* that day probably placed the Chagos MPA in the too-difficult box.

This was a crisis but I realised that it was also an opportunity for our about-to-be-formed Blue Marine Foundation, BLUE for short. Some $5 million (£3.5 million) was needed to fund protection of the reserve for a whole five-year term and to substitute for the money raised previously from selling fishing licences. Our team included film producers used to finding those sorts of sums quickly. We had five months. George said that for speed we should only approach those for whom that kind of money was small change – a very short list. It would need an overwhelmingly attractive proposition. George's pitch for the rich was: 'For the price of a house in London you can have a marine reserve you can see from space.' He and Chris went to work. My job was to convince the Foreign Office that there was a chance of the money turning up.

William Marsden, the chairman of the Chagos Conservation Trust, advised me to write to the head of Overseas Territories, who was happy to meet me, after the consultation had closed. George, meanwhile, made contact with a Swiss billionaire who had seen our film and who had raced two teams in the America's Cup. Ernesto Bertarelli saw the point of saving the ocean and was enthused by the opportunity but needed time to mobilise his family trust. I told David Miliband via his team to 'Hold on, the money is coming.' On Good Friday, the Bertarelli family said they were prepared to take on the additional cost of policing the reserve for five years. We told Miliband's office that day. Easter Monday came and went. On the Wednesday after Easter, Gordon Brown, the prime minister, was obliged to call a general election. On Tuesday afternoon, Miliband announced that he was creating the Chagos marine reserve. We had pulled it off.

We will have to wait until the secret government papers are published in 30 years' time to find out how critical our offer of funding was but I believe it made the decision easier for Miliband and pushed the government into creating the world's largest marine reserve. We had done our bit for some of the most pristine parts of the ocean. Chagos was, for now, to be a fully protected area – apart from a recreational and subsistence fishing zone around Diego Garcia. The $5 million would pay for a patrol vessel over the next five years – and the UK government would foot the bill thereafter. On the back of the creation of the first large-scale no-take reserve in the UK Overseas Territories, we were able to campaign over the next five years for protected areas to be established around all 14 of the UK Overseas Territories – if their residents liked the idea.

People may say we conservationists were naive to go ahead, given the disputed ownership of the Chagos. I think we were calculatedly realistic. We knew the creation of a vast marine reserve in the middle of a great, heavily exploited ocean would not only be an insurance policy for that ocean's biodiversity but could inspire the creation of other massive marine reserves everywhere. We knew that a new balance between conservation and subsistence fishing might have to be struck in the Chagos one day, if Mauritius prevailed or the wronged Chagossians were to return – but at least the reefs and Chagos's abundant marine resources would be in good condition and the precedent of conservation would have been set. In the meantime, a Chagos reserve would provide a touchstone for the world to show what a fully functioning tropical ecosystem should look like, both as a refuge for highly migratory fish, including 'charismatic megafauna' such as great hammerhead sharks, and as a rare example of healthy reefs and coral reef fish in profusion – though we knew these would be increasingly challenged by climate change in the decades ahead.

For the ocean at that time, it is probably not an overstatement to say the creation of the world's largest no-take reserve was a moment not unlike the creation of one of the great American national parks. It established a precedent for the UK Overseas Territories and for the world. The politician responsible in this case, David Miliband, received pivotal support from private sector funders who have since, to their credit, spent millions on research. That public–private dynamic represented a new step: a hugely positive precedent in saving our seas. Along the way, we had defined a way of working which Mark Rose, who was to be the second chairman of BLUE, would call 'strategic opportunism'. We carried the baton a short way to the finish. Other players, such as Charles Sheppard from Warwick University, who had studied the waters of Chagos most of his life, carried it for far longer and deserve much more of the credit. Yet we all, in our separate ways, played a role in getting it over the line. Whatever happened in future, we had done our best to safeguard, for now, some of the marine wonders of the world.

The question then was what dynamism we could inject into the protection of waters closer to home.

3

The Battle for England's Coral Garden

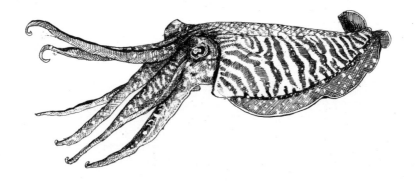

'A fisherman always sees another fisherman from afar.'

Russian proverb

LYME BAY

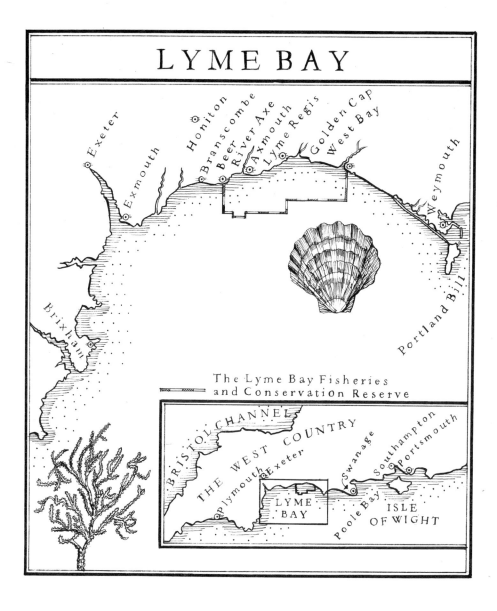

Exeter
Exmouth
Honiton
Branscombe
Beer
River Axe
Axmouth
Lyme Regis
Golden Cap
West Bay
Weymouth
Portland Bill
Brixham

The Lyme Bay Fisheries
and Conservation Reserve

BRISTOL CHANNEL
THE WEST COUNTRY
Plymouth
Exeter
Swanage
Southampton
Portsmouth
LYME
BAY
Poole Bay
ISLE
OF WIGHT

The conundrum, if you want to 'rewild' the busy seas in a populous country like the United Kingdom, is how to contend with the public right to fish. This means that the entirety of a country's territorial waters may be fished using the most fiendishly intensive measures technology can devise – unless those methods have been specifically excluded by law. That is why conservation measures that protect fish, mammals and plants by and large have to be a matter of statute, a daunting thing to get changed, and an even harder thing to propose, as an average citizen. Unlike on land, where landowners can decide how they are going to manage their broad acres and may encourage them to go wild, in the sea, any form of conservation which is not purely voluntary requires a statutory instrument, a law or bylaw, restricting or guiding what can happen in a particular place. Yet there are examples where grassroots efforts have forced the hands of the key decision makers – where the small fish have taken on the big fish. That is precisely what happened in Lyme Bay, when a group of local fishermen, with the backing of two wildlife trusts, applied pressure on ministers and dredgers in a pledge to save their sea.

Lyme Bay looks on the chart like a large bite out of the south coast of England. Above the tide mark, it is one of the most spectacular landscapes in Britain. Its shoreline of pebble and sand beaches, cliffs, downs and woodland, from Portland Bill in Dorset to Start Point in Devon, is like a picture postcard in good weather but it can be a very different place when the prevailing south-westerly wind gets up. Lyme Bay includes part of Britain's only natural World Heritage Site, known as the Jurassic Coast. Many of the earliest discoveries of fossils, which prompted theories of evolution, were made around the hilly seaside town of Lyme Regis and its neighbour Charmouth. The Cobb, the harbour wall in Lyme Regis, is celebrated in literature as the setting of the scene in Jane Austen's novel *Persuasion* where Louisa has a fall, and where Sarah Woodruff, the heroine of John Fowles's *The French Lieutenant's Woman*, stared out to sea. From the cliffs of the Golden Cap, the highest point on the south coast, on a clear day you can see across the bay to Dartmoor. As far as terrestrial landscapes are concerned, the surroundings of Lyme Bay are as about remarkable as they come.

Given all that was known about Lyme Bay and its geology, and the history that lies beneath its waves in the number of historic wrecks marked on the charts, it is surprising that it was not until the 1980s that it became widely known that the seabed itself – the extension of those rocky outcrops into the sea – held natural riches of similar importance. Divers who had swum along the reefs, which project three miles out into the bay, reported a profusion of coral: pink sea fans up to 60cm high; ross coral, which looks like giant cornflakes stuck together; white dead man's fingers and yellow sunset cup coral, found in only four other sites in Britain. While very different to the coral reefs of the tropics, with their many-coloured corals, jewel-like fish and clear waters, Lyme Bay's rocky reefs are richer than most other places in British waters – and as rich as Plymouth Sound, now the country's first national marine park – with 300 species of plants and animals below the waves, including large quantities of valuable commercial fish and shellfish. Conservationists began to call Lyme

Bay 'England's coral garden' – at the very moment its reefs began to be ground into rubble.

The alarm was sounded in the early 1990s when a survey carried out for Devon Wildlife Trust found that at least 10 per cent of Lyme Bay's reefs, an area totalling around 77 square miles, had been altered recently by scallop dredging. Until the mid-1980s, scallop dredges (steel cages which are dragged along the bottom, several at a time) could only be used on sand and gravel. Eventually, as the other beds were exhausted, fishermen perfected spring-loaded dredges and rock-hopper trawls that jumped over the rocks and made it possible to fish where only pots and static nets had been before. This technological development made the case for conservation urgent. The reefs were being turned into what one scientist has described as a building site. It was the start of a battle between local inshore fishermen – backed by conservationists – and a mix of local and nomadic industrial scalloping vessels.

The first moment that Dave Sales, a lobster fisherman, became aware there was a problem was on a glorious sunny day just before Whitsun back in 1985. The sea was calm where he was fishing three miles off West Bay, Dorset. Dave's inboard engine was idling as he hauled crab and lobster pots from the seabed onto the deck of his boat, the *Sea Dragon*. On the end of each string of pots, 150 fathoms long, floated a buoy and a flag, so the gear could be found again and the pots identified as his. Dave used his hydraulic winch to haul up the pots, then sorted the lobsters and crabs into separate boxes for sale to a local fish merchant and for the fish restaurant run by his wife, Gill. Then he put the engine in gear and carefully laid fresh pots, baited with gurnard, on the seabed, stretching out each string straight so it didn't tangle on the ground. At around 11 in the morning, in an area of Lyme Bay known as High Ledge, he looked up and to his surprise saw a fleet of 16 large fishing vessels on the horizon, coming his way.

Dave had no immediate apprehension of trouble for he was used to being passed by trawlers that gave his fishing gear a respectful berth. This fleet was different. Though Dave's gear was all clearly marked, these vessels, which he recognised as scallop dredgers, advanced alarmingly close as if they had not seen any warning. When they were almost upon him, Dave waved and pointed, but the dredgers proceeded straight through the flags, the buoys and the pots he had laid. Dave was certain they saw something. It was hard not to. They just didn't want to see it. The scallopers roared on, their great engines throbbing, steel lines straining out behind them. On the end of each steel line were four heavy-toothed dredges which stirred the scallops up off the seabed and into their nets. It was not difficult to imagine what the dredges were doing to the seabed flora and fauna and to the crabs and lobsters the inshore fishermen depended on for their living. The seabed was reduced to rubble and those creatures living on it that could not swim were mangled beyond recognition.

That day nothing was going to distract the Brixham mob from the pursuit of valuable king and queen scallops on the rocky bottom, though Dave made his feelings felt as loudly as he could. He had just managed to keep the scallopers away from the gear he was still attached to by throwing out 100 yards of floating rope to stop their advance. That, as one of their skippers shouted to him angrily, could foul their propellors and leave their 15-metre boats crippled and having to pay to be salvaged or towed back to port. Dave knew this perfectly well. He stood his ground until they backed off. The nomads grudgingly changed course a fraction and roared on, their dredges gouging the uneven ground beneath.

When Dave found himself alone again, he went back to the pots that had been left behind. They came up in bundles, tangled, twisted, with their hoops bent and broken and their netting torn off. 'Scallopers are a different breed,' said Dave. 'If they think there's scallops under somebody's pots, they just don't care, they have to go at them. They leave their brains behind in the fridge.' Dave had 40 pots mangled and torn that day, but he did recover them. He found crabs mutilated with broken-off limbs. The dredgers were making wads of money but they were destroying everyone else's livelihoods. When he returned to port in West Bay that afternoon, Dave made an angry phone call to the authorities – the officials of the Sea Fisheries Committee of the Southern region of which he was the local branch chairman – at first without much effect.

There is an alternative wisdom to that of the scientist, lawyer or conservationist which is no less valid, only different. It comes from first-hand observation over time, a lifetime of experience of the sea. Divers have it, sailors have it, fishermen and women have it and sometimes we are lucky enough that it is written down in history books. It is the brain working through the recording instrument of memory, of watching the sun go up and down and seeing what the birds do on the surface, how they interact with fish and other animals, and what is hauled up on deck over the seasons, and how that changes. Thomas Henry Huxley, one of the most prominent scientists of the late nineteenth century, made a grave error by ignoring what fishermen had told him in Royal Commission hearings when he made his proclamation on the infinite bounty of the sea in 1883. He said: 'Probably all the great sea fisheries are inexhaustible . . . that is to say, that nothing we do seriously affects the numbers of fish.' Evidence already provided by fishermen to those Royal Commissions by the time he gave that speech showed he was wrong.

Fishermen, of course, have got things wildly wrong too. They asserted that fishing was good on the Grand Banks just before the northern cod collapsed. It turned out they were fishing in a few last places where the spawning aggregations huddled together – a habit cod have when their numbers are depleted – but the fishermen didn't interpret what they were seeing correctly and Canadian government scientists, who were too close to the fishermen, believed them. All the other cod had been caught. Both forms of observation, though, contain truths which need to be evaluated, one against the other. Combined, they describe the larger truth.

I learned most of what I know about the life of an inshore fisherman from Dave. We first spoke on the phone while I was a journalist at the *Telegraph*, covering the latest developments in Lyme Bay. We even presented together at meetings and conferences, he as the fisherman, I as the conservationist. They called us Chas and Dave. We teased each other brutally but it was amiable. As we got to know each other, I wanted to hear about the things Dave had seen over the course of a lifetime at sea. We talked a lot while Dave was still fishing, and a lot more while he recovered from a stroke he had at the age of 83 which necessitated his retirement from the sea.

Passing on how fishing used to be done – compared to how it is now – was a distraction from his lack of mobility and mornings of physiotherapy. We were both energised by the task. It was my privilege to learn just how much had changed, how much wilder and more productive the sea was in his youth and how, in Dave's view, 'Technology has kept so much further ahead than conservation.'

Dave was that unusual 'Pushmi-Pullyu' kind of creature, a fisherman conservationist. He had seen an industry at its best and its worst and managed to give something back. A year before he died in March 2022 he was awarded the British Empire Medal for his work in fishing and conservation. 'Not bad,' as he would say, 'for a village boy.'

Dave grew up in Studland, a pretty village further east on the Dorset coast. Some of the rehearsals for D-Day were conducted there and it was a long time before the beach was cleared of munitions after the war. Dave remembers finally going back to the beach in 1947 and, to his delight, catching seahorses in his shrimping net. Recently, he has heard conservationists describing seahorses as 'far from their natural home off Portugal and Spain'. They assumed the seahorses had arrived because of global warming. Dave says the seahorses were always there. When he was a boy, there was an old fisherman who used to keep dried seahorses in his shed.

Only two fishermen, Gus Payne and Lew Churchill, were allowed on to the beach in wartime, to catch herring. According to them, the last of the herring was caught in 1943. The 'silver darlings' used to come in big shoals, starting up by the Isle of Wight, coming into Poole Bay, finishing up in Studland Bay around the time of Poole Fair, on 5 November. Swanage, three miles to the west of Studland, used to be the centre for processing the herring as it was on the railway. Dave had been told that one of his village's oldest fishermen, Jerry Dyke, had back in 1909 earned 35 gold sovereigns in a year from the herring. After the 1939–45 war, the herring disappeared – just like the vast shoals of mackerel that used to be seen in Lyme Bay. As Dave remembered it, 'When I was a youngster, they used to come round the villages selling mackerel. I remember my mother used to shout for me and give me two shillings and I used to go and get a bloody great plate of Weymouth mackerel.' There were 15 mackerel fishing crews in Lyme Bay, the last one around Golden Cap.

There's no mackerel in spring, no mackerel in autumn now. It seems that perhaps for once it is not just fishing to blame but also climate change. The shoals have been moving north as the water warms. The local fishmonger in West Bay has mackerel sent down from Shetland now at £2.80 a kilo. It is even being caught off Spitsbergen, in the Arctic circle.

When Dave first went to sea to earn his living in the late 1950s, navigation was by compass and a series of marks on the shore. Fishing on the south coast was a cottage industry, a far cry from what went on at the great deep-water ports of Hull and Grimsby. Dave said: 'We were still in tune with nature then. We had to make our own lobster pots. It was just past the age of willow pots but all the gear we used was made from natural fibres. It was heavier to work and took more effort to haul. We used to import chestnut hoops from France and netted them with sisal or manilla. We didn't fish in the winter. The [potting] gear would not stand it. We either did a bit of trawling or a bit of sprat catching.' Synthetic rope and net turned up in the early 1960s and changed everything. Another thing that has happened in a single lifetime that has had an impact on fishing globally are improvements in navigation, now provided by the satellite-based Global Positioning System and used on even the smallest boats.

Something else that has changed since Dave's days of apprenticeship to Maurice Lane, a skilled fisherman who fished harder than most, is how much they used to catch compared with today. They hauled the same 150 pots three times in 24 hours. By the end of the day, they would have caught 1,000lbs of lobsters. Today, the catch from 150 pots would be 50lbs, if you were fortunate. The catch per unit of effort for each individual fishing boat has declined massively.

Back in the early 1960s, when he acquired his own boat, Dave and his crew were the rising stars of the south coast, catching sprats in the winter by pair-trawling with another vessel, a technique which allows a large mid-water net to be used, held wide open by the distance between the two vessels. There are pictures of them up to their waists in sprats. Dave found big sprats under the Needles at the Isle of Wight, where they used to rise out of the rocks on slack water. The sprats came into Lyme Bay, too; there are similar pictures of Jim Newton from Beer and his family around the same time, decks awash with sprats. The sprats have not gone away. What has gone is the inshore fishermen's entitlement to catch them.

A huge injustice was done to the inshore fleet in the mid-1990s, when conservation legislation began to bite and the UK government was required by Europe to allocate a quota to its fleet in an attempt to control catches. The quota was allocated to the over-ten-metre fleet on the basis of documented track record. The inshore fleet, which makes up 75 per cent of the boats fishing in English waters today, did not have its track record adequately documented. So the largest number of active fishermen – roughly 7,000 of them out of 12,000 – were allocated a measly 4 per cent of the total UK quota of commercially caught species. This blunder has still to be rectified.

This explains why so many inshore boats are nowadays dependent on shellfish and other species that are not subject to quota, such as cuttlefish and whelk, and why these species are getting hammered one after another. Quota can be bought at a price, as it has become a tradeable commodity, but quota has also been speculated upon by the 'slipper skippers' – fishermen who have sold their boats but still own quota – and working commercial firms who inherited it based on their track record, making it verging on unaffordable for a small-boat owner. The result is that one boat in Lyme Bay can have 3 tonnes of quota for sole and the boat fishing beside it can have 30 kilos. Huge shoals of unidentified fish still show up on the fish finder out in the Channel today, which could be sprat, pout or even herring, but no inshore fishermen has the quota to catch them. It may be that there is no good economic reason to do so either. Tastes in fish have changed and economics play a large part in the attrition, or neglect, that wild fish face.

There were fewer fishing boats in the 1960s and 1970s, Dave recalled, probably because few had the money to build them. As a result, the attrition of nature was less than it is today. Certain species of fish have disappeared since then as a result of fishing pressure, starting with the common skate. Dave hadn't heard of one being caught on the south coast for 50–60 years. Off the Golden Cap in Lyme Bay, there used to be sand shark, now gone. No one actively targeted them, so he assumed that they were fished out as bycatch. Certain other species of fish have arrived. From the late 1960s they began to catch triggerfish in pots. Probably because the sea was warmer, thought Dave. 'We had trouble getting the fish out past the mouth of the pots. They have a spike on them like a unicorn. That was the first time we thought things were altering a bit, climate-wise.' The latest absence is the brown crab, a staple quarry, which used to migrate along the coast and which shows little sign of returning at present.

In the late 1960s, Dave became aware of the vulnerability of his main quarry, the lobster. He won a Churchill scholarship to study it on the east coast of the United States, in the Maritime Provinces and on the west coast of Canada. He found the North Americans used a far more accurate measurement for the minimum landing size than the UK. Measuring the carapace, from eye socket to the back, was a better indication of maturity than stretching the lobster out and measuring it from nose to tail. Returning those lobsters whose carapace was too short ensured the female could bear eggs once or twice before being caught. Dave brought these improve-ments back, persuaded the authorities to adopt them and they are in use today. As a result of his work, and the Southern Sea Fisheries Committee's, all berried lobsters – females with eggs – must be returned to the water in the area. In other parts of the UK, the Channel Islands and France, they still land berried lobsters to this day. No wonder that in those places, fishermen have to work far harder to make a living than they do now in Lyme Bay. Dave believed another great conservation measure was that Southern set the maximum size of fishing vessel it would license at 12 metres, compared with 15 metres further west in Devon and Cornwall. A bigger boat can carry a bigger engine, more gear, more crew and fish in worse weather, so inevitably it catches more and potentially causes more damage to the seabed.

The one indelible stain on the Southern Fisheries Committee's good record was the overfishing of the native oyster in the Solent, which separates the south coast from the Isle of Wight. Dave and his crew dabbled at oyster fishing in the 1970s. He could see where it was going, though. As a member of the Sea Fisheries Committee, he had to defend its unsuccessful attempts to impose order. Dave recalled, 'How they ruined that fishery was incredible. What a disgusting lot of fishermen they were. They weren't fishermen. The tricks that they would use to get the oysters out of there behind our backs. They made their money by poaching the bloody things. If there is a fiddle going, fishermen are in on it.' Dave wasn't afraid of saying so. He gave an interview to the *Bournemouth Daily Echo* in 1976. The headline was: 'Fishing: an industry ruined by greed.'

Overall, in Dave's view, the problem with the sea today was that there were fewer places for wild animals to hide; fewer times when fishermen were not at sea; the gear was lighter and more durable and the technology available to fishermen was better and more deadly. The task for conservation, he believed, was to put back some of the challenges for the fishermen that made the sea more productive in the past.

His verdict on the last 70 years: 'I think we overdone it a bit.'

*

The campaign that began the day Dave had his first confrontation with the scallopers off West Bay was to last 23 years. It would involve fishermen, wildlife trusts, nature conservation agencies, politicians, divers, journalists like myself and members of the public, who became aware of the shocking damage that the fleets of dredgers were doing to the living successors of the ammonite fossils that still turn up on the Jurassic coast. Reports highlighted the importance of the Lyme Bay reefs for their corals and other wildlife and in 1998, Devon Wildlife Trust carried out a comprehensive survey, with fishermen on the project steering group, and identified the reefs due south of Lyme Regis as the most fragile and in danger of disturbance.

In 2000–1, the Southern Sea Fisheries Committee considered imposing a bylaw to protect reef features but this was hotly opposed by big-vessel representatives. The committee concluded that a voluntary approach was more likely to succeed. It suggested that the Wildlife Trust, the South West Fish Producers' Organisation, which represented the scallopers, and local fishermen develop a voluntary agreement to protect the reefs by closing two areas, Lanes Ground and Saw Tooth Ledges, to dredging and trawling. The first of several voluntary agreements was reached.

The last agreement held for only a matter of weeks. Higher prices for scallops and the development of West Bay harbour, which allowed overnight stays for fishing vessels from outside the area, led to an increase in the number of scalloping boats in the bay from 9 to 20. Some were travelling from as far as Cornwall to take advantage of the scallop stocks. The increased competition led to allegations that the voluntary agreement had broken down and scallopers were fishing the sensitive parts of the reefs. However, Natural England, the government's conservation advisers, an official body that hitherto had more experience dealing with the land than the sea, never managed to prove its allegations to the satisfaction of ministers. As a senior government official, Rodney Anderson, later said, why would the scallopers break an agreement when they had been warned that they would be thrown out of the area?

It certainly wasn't the local Lyme Regis families who broke the agreement. It was they who had most to lose. In 2006, Natural England applied for a Ministerial Stop Order to close 60 square miles of Lyme Bay to dredging to allow the damaged seabed to recover. It was not granted because the Department for the Environment, Food and Rural Affairs was critical of the feeble nature of the evidence put forward by Natural England, which was submitted on just a page and a half of A4 paper. All the same, in August that year, the government boasted that it had concluded an agreement with the South West Inshore Scallopers Association to voluntarily close less than a quarter of the threatened area, 'protecting 90 per cent of the area where pink sea fans occur'. Natural England and Devon Wildlife Trust took the unusual step of challenging the government's decision.

Public concern about Lyme Bay grew the following year after the deliberate beaching of the storm-damaged container ship MSC *Napoli* at Branscombe, to save it from breaking up and causing a worse environmental disaster. Oil was spilled, which affected some seabirds. Some 103 containers fell into the sea and hundreds of people went onto the beach to salvage flotsam, which included BMW motorcycles, nappies, perfume and car parts.

The following year, 2008, Dave Sales and his wife Gill went to London for the Shellfish Association of Great Britain meeting. With them they took a file containing nine photographs showing the seabed before and after scalloping and handed it in at Number 10 Downing Street, addressed to the prime minister, Gordon Brown. A friendly policeman allowed Dave to knock on the door. The file was returned a few weeks later with a note saying a copy had been passed to the fisheries minister, Jonathan Shaw. The two events may or may not be connected but later that year, Shaw announced a statutory instrument protecting 60 square miles of Lyme Bay from trawling and dredging. Finally: triumph! It was the largest ever closure in British waters to protect wildlife.

Rodney Anderson, who was the director of fisheries at the time, was the only senior official in the room at the moment Shaw took that decision. Rodney recalls that it was not allegations of illegal scallop fishing that swayed the minister but evidence of the nature conservation value of what was on the seabed. He and the minister then called a meeting of the scallop boats and their associations in Lyme Regis and told them that the decision to close the area had not been taken because of anything they had done. 'We felt we had to go down there and tell them that because they had adhered to their side of the bargain. But when you looked at what was down there and the nature conservation advice on what should be protected, that was the decisive factor. We called the meeting because we felt we had to look them in the eye and tell them that.'

Reactions to the closure were sharply polarised. The fishing industry – the most visible part of it at least, which represented the scallopers – was stunned that the minister had acted as he had.

Conservationists were triumphant. Joan Edwards, marine conservation officer for the Wildlife Trusts, said when the closure was announced: 'This is our national park moment. This is effectively the first marine national park and the largest area to be protected for its wildlife anywhere in the UK.' For Dave Sales and other small-boat inshore fishermen, who together with the two wildlife trusts had faced bitter and public personal criticism from the scallopers but continued to make their case, it was a satisfying result which had taken many years to achieve.

Lyme Bay seemed very important to us as a new conservation charity. By an accident of crisis management, the government had imposed more effective restrictions over a larger area than they had dared to do just about anywhere else in the country.[1] There, the public right to fish had been faced down for the public benefit. It was one of a handful of places where this had happened in the country and by far the largest, busiest and one of the richest in terms of marine life. This de facto marine park in Lyme Bay needed to be supported and to be a success, as that would lead to more like it being created. The fishermen who had promoted it deserved to be seen as local heroes. But unfortunately this was not what happened first.

Tim Glover was my business partner in a couple of ventures after I left the *Daily Telegraph* and he came with me when BLUE was formed. When he and I went to Lyme Bay, three years after the closure to dredging, we did not find happy fishermen or a recovering marine environment. There was dissatisfaction and disillusionment among the very fishermen who had supported the closure, for all sorts of reasons. As yet, there was no obvious recovery of the seabed fauna, or the commercial or other species that lived upon it, even of the scallops, which one of the scallop divers present at our first meeting, 'Blond John' Worswick, used to harvest every day. Bad blood remained between the inshore fishermen and the scallop dredgers who had been excluded and the local big-boat fishermen who had been forced to go elsewhere. There were illegal, nocturnal incursions from dredgers. The inshore fishermen – Dave and his colleagues – would have nothing to do with the Wildlife Trusts who had pulled off the coup of getting the reefs protected and then, as the fishermen saw it, walked away. The officials of the newly created Southern Inshore Fisheries and Conservation Authority were understandably preoccupied with setting up a new statutory body and had yet to work out how to manage the largest no-trawl zone in the country.

The inshore fleet also had the usual complaint, one that you can hear all round the country to this day. The small, under-ten-metre boats had too little access to quota for sole, ray, bass and other fin fish – big boats and foreign fleets had the vast majority of it. On top of that, many fishermen resented the fact that they had given up other potential ways of fishing (many had trawled or dredged them-selves in the past) for no benefit or recognition from the community or the public at large. The market was not paying them any premium for fishing from small boats with limited amounts of gear and their fish and shellfish were fetching poor prices, for reasons that none of us then understood.

We heard something else that troubled us. Overfishing was tak-ing place even now. The removal of trawling and dredging meant that the area had become a magnet for large quantities of static gear – pots and nets. At the Devon end of the bay, where larger, 15-metre vessels were allowed due to the county's different rules, there was one large vessel with a crew of three laying several thousand pots a week, which was causing resentment among fishermen in the ports of Beer and Axmouth. (The Lyme Bay reefs are half in Devon, half in Dorset, which means there are different rules depending on if you turn left or right out of Lyme Regis harbour.) Jim Newton, a fisherman with his own fish shop in Beer, said his catches had fallen 50 per cent since the closure of the reefs to trawling and dredging because of the arrival of all this static gear. This, we thought, was the ultimate absurdity: a marine protected area that had by then taken more than 25 years to set up was being overfished, but in a different way. It was probable that the huge number of pots and nets was starting to impact on the protected features of the reef. It would have been better, from a nature conservation perspective, to ban fishing altogether – except that this wasn't acceptable to the traditional fishing communities who plied their trade in the four ports along Lyme Bay.

There was a chance we could make things better. We asked a lobster fisherman from Portland, Neville Copperthwaite, to set up a meeting at the café in West Bay, which was attended by Dave Sales and about 15 other fishermen. I suggested to them that if this conservation area, effectively Britain's first marine national park, was to succeed and to spawn others, fishermen should get something out of it. They deserved public recognition for fishing sustainably and within natural limits – they were local heroes. They liked this idea. But we also recommended they create a large no-take zone to enhance the conservation value of the area, in return for some assistance to label their produce as traceable and sustainably caught, to attract a premium price. The no-take-zone part of this idea went down badly. Dave Hancock from Axmouth growled: 'That's the thin end of the wedge.'

On the train back to London, Tim and I tore up lots of our ideas and prioritised the ones where we were aligned with the fishermen. What they wanted was not so unreasonable. They wanted respect and recognition for their light-touch fishing methods and an end to the perceived attack on their way of life from environmentalists – of which I was one. They wanted guaranteed access to fish and shellfish in return for proof that the ways they fished were indeed sustainable. And they wanted the big boats with several thousand pots from outside the area to go away.

We decided we would do conservation the fishermen's way. The core of what they wanted, we wanted. There would have to be a 'win' for fishing, a 'win' for conservation and a 'win' for local communities. We all desperately hoped that this prototype multi-use marine national park would work.

We began to cohere. The Lyme Bay Working Group held its meetings at the Royal Lion Hotel in Lyme Regis in the evenings, with drinks and sandwiches for the fishermen who had come straight from the dock. Visiting speakers came from far away, including the US NGO the Environmental Defence Fund. We even organised an exchange with a project in Morro Bay, California, where conservationists had bought out the fishing rights and sold them back to fishermen, provided they used hooks, not trawls. The group became a kind of university of fishing and conservation. Attendance grew.

Once we had agreed our objectives, we figured we needed political support. We reached out to Oliver Letwin, the local Dorset MP, who was already sympathetic, and the fisheries minister, Richard Benyon, to try to solidify our work into legislation. We also needed support for science. We went to Defra's chief scientist, Dr Bob Watson, who agreed to fund what turned out to be a four-year study by the University of Plymouth under Professor Martin Attrill into the effects of potting in protected areas. The study was to test whether potting – at the level of one man, one boat, according to the voluntary code – would have an impact on the reefs and the corals on Lyme Bay's seabed. We got our no-take zones, albeit very small ones, named 'control areas'. Honour was satisfied.

As we and the fishermen got to know each other, there were more discoveries. The first, when we tried to get a better price for their fish, was that at the time, the quality – the freshness and shelf life – of Lyme Bay fish was not very good. We and EDF invited along the fish auctioneers of Plymouth and Brixham, who told our small-boat fishermen that they did indeed pay higher prices, around 30 per cent in fact, to some named vessels who looked after their fish properly. They said there was a tendency in Lyme Bay to use too little ice and to leave the fish out for collection under an oily rag for hours before a man finally came and took it to auction. No buyer was going to pay a premium for the provenance of fish if it was not the freshest of fresh. That meant icing it at sea, which apparently the majority of fishermen in under-ten-metre boats were not doing. So we invested in ice boxes, chiller rooms and even, eventually, a lobster store at Axmouth. The idea there was that fishermen did not have to store their lobsters at sea in poor weather after which they would emerge bruised or dead. Ten years on, we have a 'man and van' scheme which takes the fishermen's produce to market in Plymouth. The aim is to develop outlets in London and Cheltenham which pay an extra premium for branded 'Lyme Bay Reserve Seafood' with quality and provenance. The original idea is finally coming together under the eye of BLUE's California-born project manager, Mandy Wolfe.

A few years into the project, nature did us the biggest favour of all. A great recovery began. It started about four years after the dredgers had been banned, then it accelerated. Dr Emma Sheehan from the University of Plymouth, who has monitored the reefs since the closure in 2008, said she couldn't at first see why the reefs she began to study had been protected, as so much of them looked like a building site. Then, after a time, the forests of creatures on the seabed began to grow. The sea fans, the dead man's fingers and other corals returned.

Then, abruptly, came a huge natural setback. In the winter of 2013–14, the growth on the seabed was flattened by storms of astonishing intensity from the south west. Fishermen lost gear, had it smashed up or washed away. It taught us how brutal the forces of nature can be – everything was smashed back to rubble again with a fury apparently far greater than dredgers could have summoned. But the benign powers of nature returned and it all grew back, measurably quicker than it had recovered after dredging was banned – the building blocks of recovery were somehow still there. With the corals came more species, including more valuable fish than before and scallops in profusion.

Twelve years after the closure to dredging, Plymouth's researchers say that the number of fish species inside the protected area is now more than four times what it is outside its boundaries.[2] Their baited video cameras also recorded an abundance of commercially valuable fish – gurnard, conger eel, dab, turbot, red mullet, pollack, thornback ray, catshark, huss, sole, seabream, horse mackerel, pout and John Dory – nearly four times greater than in similar areas outside where bottom-towed fishing methods are still permitted. Over the same period, whelk and lobster numbers have altered very little, indicating that they had not been overfished. The number of reef-living ross corals and pink sea fans that the 2008 closure was intended to protect has increased to a small extent compared with a drastic decline in those species elsewhere – so the closure has done the job of nature conservation it was meant to do. Outside the protected area, there are fewer fish and shellfish species but still many more than elsewhere, implying that there is a kind of overspill effect. Unfortunately, though, the news of recovery soon got around and there have been problems recently with Cornish nomads coming in, catching sole with vast lengths of net and breaking the voluntary code, but this is a problem the committee of fishermen and regulators that we set up is duly taking on.

For a time, the fishing for the small boats of Lyme Bay in the newly recovered area was very good. Fishermen told researchers they were happier. They caught more for less effort. Anglers were gruntled too. As Mike Spiller, from Honiton Sea Angling Club and a member of the committee, wrote: 'The fishing in and around the reserve has improved no end. We now have bigger and better fish to catch and release and also new species arriving more frequently. Well done.' The ten-year journey we embarked upon was filmed by Rupert Murray, the director of *The End of the Line*, who shot a film for us called *Lyme Bay: Road to Recovery.* The feedback from the fishermen was positive.

Looking back, it must be said the lion's share of the credit for the success of the Lyme Bay protected area, and the recovery, belongs to those responsible for pushing through the closure of the reefs in 2008: Jonathan Shaw, Rodney Anderson, the Wildlife Trusts and fishermen such as Dave Sales. The BLUE project that came along afterwards consolidated and recorded that ecological improvement and gave something back to the fishing communities affected in terms of better prices and better access to the market in return for keeping fishing pressure under control. The project, at its best, brought significantly greater agreement between conservationists and fishermen than exists elsewhere and put the fishermen in the driving seat in deciding conservation methods. They are the experts on what works with the grain of fishing. The goodwill involved, unusual between fishermen and conservationists, brought about a significant recovery that would probably not have happened otherwise. There are many things still to tackle but Lyme Bay is an example of getting things right, most of the time, provided that a protected area which encompasses fishing is fished in a small-scale and sustainable way.

To what extent can Lyme Bay be said to be 'rewilded'? That is hard to answer. Some might say that Lyme Bay was an example of why absolute protection is unnecessary and that 'rewilding' can be achieved as long as fishing is conducted within carefully defined sustainable limits. Others would warn, as did Dave Sales, that technological improvements and human ingenuity will always get ahead of conservation unless there is continued, vigilant management.

Certainly, the recovery that was seen in Lyme Bay was comparable in some ways to what has been seen in some of the few fully protected areas without fishing at all, such as Lamlash Bay on the Isle of Arran. The fully protected areas are by a margin better, of course, but does it matter?

Lyme Bay remains an example of the 'art of the possible', rather than the absolute, as far as rewilding is concerned. It shows how biodiversity can be preserved where fishing remains inevitable. Many of the species within it – the rays, the cuttlefish, the bass – remain overfished because of what goes on at a larger scale outside the reserve, which comes down to poor fisheries management elsewhere. The large species that were once present – the sand sharks and common skate – are gone. Lyme Bay's de facto marine park remains a work in progress. The Lyme Bay MPA remains, however, the UK's first and largest example of an ambitious, whole-site approach to marine protection, which was designed to manage, recover and aid biodiversity by considering the whole ecosystem. That is an achievement. More science is needed to define a way of netting within the reserve and outside that will not put stocks under pressure. That work would not be needed if the area was not fished at all but the communities clearly want it to be, so we will have to find a way to get the work done.

There is even more to do. One day it would be good to see Lyme Bay become a marine national park, with maybe a core area fully protected from all fishing. Some fishermen back that idea now – though many, like Dave, resisted the idea of that no-take area at its core. I think they are persuadable, given the right offer – such as a no-trawl zone from Portland Bill to Start Point, right across the mouth of the Bay, and a grant of enough quota by the government to fish it profitably.

Lyme Bay shows that nature has an enormous powers of recovery, if you remove the most damaging fishing gear and keep the rest under control. At the moment that control is wavering – an uplift in the amount of sole that can be caught has brought in vessels from outside the area – but I think the community will pull together again. It would be better if the voluntary code had some legislative backbone – this may come. It would be better, too, if there was a limit on the boats that can fish in the area. We continue to work towards these goals and towards the harmonisation of people and the rules. With all those reservations and caveats, Lyme Bay remains a model for managing not just protected areas but all coastal waters.

Rory Moore, a colleague of mine, arranged an exchange visit for fishers from all over the Mediterranean to come to Lyme Bay – including from a successful project in Turkey, similar to Lyme, but unique in the region, where the incomes of local fisherwomen have benefited after trawling was banned. When John Shuker, a Lyme Regis scallop diver, began to talk about the abundance of scallops and fish now in the bay, one of the visitors looked close to tears. Stella Stylianou, the daughter of a fisherman from Cyprus, said: 'I think your fish boxes would be invaluable for my family in Cyprus but we just can't catch enough fish to fill them – there are none left.' Nods of agreement came from around the room. There is still a crisis in our seas and many places where rewilding and a return to plenty are still a dream.

4

Return of the Native (Oyster)

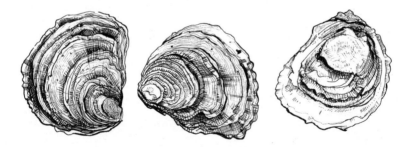

'There is a fleeting moment when you have eaten an oyster when your mouth tastes like the freshest rockpool on Earth and that's why you do it. Suddenly you are most wonderfully refreshed and then it's gone.'

Peter Marren on *Natural Histories*, BBC Radio 4, 2016

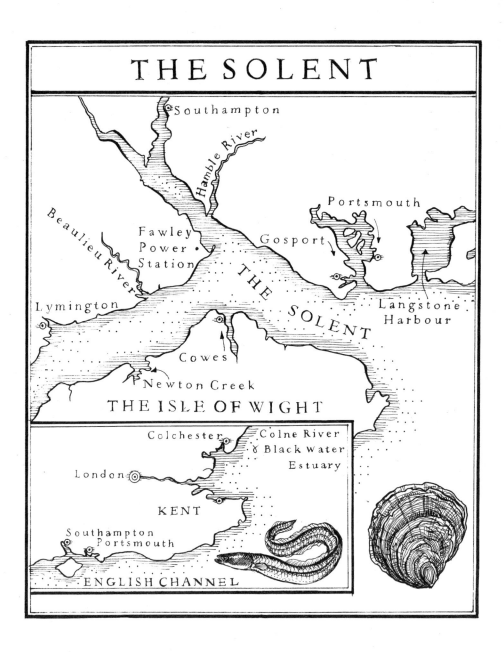

THE SOLENT

Southampton

Hamble River

Portsmouth

Beaulieu River

Fawley
Power
Station

Gosport

THE

Lymington

SOLENT

Cowes

Langstone
Harbour

Newton Creek

THE ISLE OF WIGHT

Colchester

Colne River
& Black water
Estuary

London

KENT

Southampton
Portsmouth

ENGLISH CHANNEL

I have always loved eating oysters, for the reasons so well expressed by one of my favourite nature writers, Peter Marren. It wasn't hard to be interested in the role they play in the ecosystem, or the story of their exploitation. I knew that the species most commonly eaten throughout the world, even fresh from the apparently wild lochs of Scotland, was the crinkly-shelled Pacific species, *Crassostrea gigas*, originally from Japan, which grow much faster than the native European flat oyster, *Ostrea edulis*.[1] Living, as I do, near Colchester where there has been a continuous tradition of native oyster cultivation in the estuaries of the rivers Colne and Blackwater since, and almost certainly before, the Roman occupation, I also knew that the native flat oyster sold for a higher price. This made sense for they were harder to get and more delicious. What I had suspected but only confirmed when I read some of the latest scientific papers – for some reason a previous generation of academics had euphemised and equivocated about it – was that the fate that befell the native European flat oyster, and other native species of oyster around the world, was usually a clear case of overfishing. When I found that out, it seemed that the oyster's survival was something our marine charity should be taking a close interest in.

The native oyster, as I shall call *Ostrea edulis* from now on, seems to have been ubiquitous around the Mediterranean, north-east Atlantic and North Sea coasts 1,000 years ago. It was eaten in quantity from the earliest times: the oldest middens of discarded shells found in Europe are on the Danish coast and date to around 5,000 BC. It was pretty easy to harvest oysters even before the advent of dredges, whether towed by sail or steam – all you needed to do was wade into the sea with a rake. It is fair to assume that an enormous number of oyster grounds disappeared well before the Industrial Revolution. By 1850, native oysters were being harvested in unbelievable plenty, with some 500 million a year apparently being sold across London markets. They were then very cheap and the food of the poor. When oyster beds were fished out, attempts were made to re-stock the oysters by moving them from places where they were still abundant. This disguised the rapine that was going on. Essex and Kent oystermen both bought native flat oysters from the Solent to replenish their broodstock. The Solent was supplied from Brittany in the 1920s. Another largely undocumented source of oysters was from deep water in the English Channel, where O.T. Olsen's *Piscatorial Atlas* of 1883 shows oyster beds now largely eradicated by trawling and scallop dredging, though I have heard of dredgers coming across a bed of them out in the Channel from time to time even recently. Olsen's map also shows huge oyster beds, 200 nautical miles long, in the central North Sea, in an area still known as the Oyster Grounds. These deep-water oysters, which seem to have reproduced even more slowly than coastal oysters, were fished out by the mid-1930s.

Over the past millennium, it is estimated that over 90 per cent of the oyster beds that once existed in the world have gone. With them went the invisible but significant benefits that they brought to the whole marine ecosystem. For the wonderfully mysterious thing about oysters is their ability to attract other marine life. This ability was first described by Karl Möbius, a German zoologist, in the natural oyster beds of the Bay of Kiel in the 1860s. Möbius coined the expression 'biocenosis', meaning the interaction of organisms living together in a habitat, 50 years before the word 'ecosystem' was invented. Möbius was intensely aware of the interconnected ecosystem that was about to be lost on the shores of the Wadden Sea. He wrote: 'As man has uprooted the greatest forests, so he can also annihilate the richest oyster beds.' This duly happened to the ones Möbius had described. There seem to be very few, if any, examples of people managing oyster beds successfully over long periods, except in the private grounds of Essex and Kent and one or two Scottish sea lochs.

It is a curious paradox that the native oyster would be thought of as a domesticated creature were it not for this mysterious ability to create habitat. It has been moved around and interbred so much with oysters from other places that it is probably best described as a mongrel. But oysters, even introduced Pacific oysters which have run wild in recent years, all seem to have the ability to gather other species around them. By reintroducing native oysters, or nurturing the few remaining oysters there are left in places where there are enough of them, one is not just restoring a single species but an entire ecosystem. According to research by the University of Portsmouth, an astonishing 466 species are associated with native oyster beds. This makes the native oyster what scientists call a keystone species – an organism that helps define an ecosystem. So, we figured, oyster restoration was one of the best things you could possibly do if you wanted to rewild the seas around our shores.

You may wonder how we fell into the business of oyster

restoration. I sometimes ask myself the same question, for it has turned out to be a massive undertaking, but a rewarding one. What happened was that after one of our meetings in Lyme Bay, Rob Clark, chief executive of the Southern Inshore Fisheries and Conservation Authority, stayed on for a drink in the bar of the Royal Lion hotel. With some understatement, Rob said he had a bit of a problem and wondered if we could help. The problem, it turned out, was that he had had to close the fishery for oysters in the Solent that year for the first time due to the collapse of the stock and he was wondering if we could help the IFCA bring the oyster back.

The stock that had collapsed was the last remnant of the very same native oysters that Dave Sales had accused his fellow fishermen of fishing out through sheer greed back in the late 1970s. Fishing had continued in one or two places by a dwindling number of vessels, with the season eventually lasting only days, but, in the end, catches had just dropped off the graph. The IFCA decided it had a duty to close the fishery in the faint hope of preserving what few oysters were left. Thus came to an end the largest remaining oyster fishery in Europe, which had employed as many as 700 oyster fishermen as recently as the 1970s. The hardship the collapse of the oyster caused to the few remaining oyster fishermen was evident but the damage did not end there. A single adult oyster can filter up to an astonishing 140 litres of water a day, so the removal of the oysters had caused a spiral of decline with the water becoming more prone to algal blooms, as excess nutrients entering the sea are no longer removed by filtration. Green algae now smothers mudflats, seagrass and salt-marsh edges. Water companies, meanwhile, did not invest in water quality improvements that would have accelerated oyster recovery. By then, some other big companies that used to own fishing rights over 'private grounds' in the Solent had abandoned them and a 'tragedy of the commons' had ensued. The Solent, the 60-mile-long waterway which separates the Isle of Wight from the English mainland, was in an awful mess.

Oysters had been reintroduced to the Solent before so we figured it would work again. The first broodstock oysters we managed to get hold of in 2017 were largely fished out of the path of a 'capital dredge' which was about to be undertaken to maintain the depth of the port of Southampton. The Solent, I should explain, is a very busy waterway. It is a pleasant low-level coastline with woods and beaches and old ports. It is full of sails most days, as Cowes, the Mecca of sailing, is at its heart. Cruise ships and container vessels approach and leave the port of Southampton and Royal Navy ships arrive to dock in Portsmouth. These large ships require maintenance dredges to be dug regularly in the shallow seabed so they do not run aground. The 25,000 living oysters we paid the fishermen to remove for our broodstock would otherwise, rather shockingly, have been dredged up and dumped, entombed in the dredge spoil.

When he heard we wanted to reintroduce oysters in his back yard, the owner of a series of marinas Edward Iliffe persuaded us to try out an idea he had seen in the United States – bags of clams suspended under pontoons. This had the dual purpose of demonstrating the quality of the water and improving the productivity of the bivalves by keeping them off the bottom and away from their natural predators. In the case of the oyster in the Solent, these include the tingle, a native species of predator that attaches itself to the oyster shell and bores inside to eat the oyster. Other oyster killers are the introduced American slipper limpet, which competes for food and makes a lot of silt which can smother the oysters, and the amusingly named boring sponge, which sticks to the oyster's shell and drills holes, eventually killing it.

We were concerned that there were now so many predators and so few oysters that our oysters would be wiped out before they had a chance to breed. So, with the University of Portsmouth, we evolved an improvement on bags – a sort of vertical tubular cage or 'oyster hotel' which could be filled with broodstock oysters and dropped into slots in the pontoons. Sir Ben Ainslie was one of the first to have one of these oyster nurseries designed and installed under the pontoon of his America's Cup racing team's marina in Portsmouth. The oysters in the nurseries produced waves of larvae which were carried into the Solent in search of solid objects to attach themselves to, of which we knew there were now relatively few, due to long years of siltation and relatively few oysters dying naturally and leaving their shells behind for the oyster spat to settle on. Oyster larvae float around until they find a piece of shell or hard substrate (which could be anything but likely stones or gravel) to attach themselves to, at which point they are known as spat. They latch on and adjust their position with a foot that they re-absorb once they have selected the exact place they want to spend the rest of their lives.

It was not long before we witnessed for ourselves the native oyster's mysterious ability to aggregate other marine life. When our young team and volunteers pulled up the cages loaded with mature oysters they saw that the oysters were not alone. Cute tompot blennies, weird snake pipefish, sea squirts and nudibranchs had all snuggled in beside the oysters. Juvenile bass, spider crabs, lumpsuckers and European eels of several sizes were also recorded – so far to date, 130 species have been found in the oyster nurseries. There was even a juvenile seahorse. I knew from Dave Sales's recollections that there were seahorses on the south coast and around the Isle of Wight – actually two species, the long snouted and the short snouted. But in a marina, in a cage at the top of the water column? What was the waterborne signal that had brought the seahorse from the seagrass beds that were its home to the oyster nursery? One theory is that all these species can detect and are attracted to the chemical signals produced by the oysters.

The oyster purifies water as it feeds. It has a large stomach and gills used both to breathe and ingest food. It breathes in water, using small hairs called cilia to sort and move the particles, whether algae or other food items, down into its mouth. Before entering the digestive system, inedible matter is rejected and vomited out again as what is known as pseudofaeces. The way oysters filter their food is extraordinarily important for water quality because all particles sucked through the oyster, whether ingested or rejected, are bound together in mucus and are likely to settle out of the water column and into the sediment. In a muddy, algal place such as the Solent this is particularly valuable. If you put oysters in a tank of seawater full of green algae it will be clear within a few hours. The native oysters of Chesapeake Bay on the east coast of the United States, *Crassostrea virginica*, could once filter a volume of water equivalent to the entire bay – about 19 trillion gallons – in a week. Today, according to the Chesapeake Bay Foundation, it takes more than a year. Evidence from the United States suggests that the value of an oyster reef, if all its 'ecosystem services' such as purifying the water and stabilising the seabed are taken into account, far exceeds the value of the oysters that could be extracted from it.

It seemed extraordinary to us that there were so many native oysters in the Solent as recently as the 1970s, when *Ostrea edulis* had been hammered almost everywhere else. A report we commissioned from Lymington-based consultants MacAlister Elliott attributed this profusion to the bringing of oysters from Brittany in the 1920s, coupled with perhaps a couple of extraordinarily successful breeding seasons since then. So why did the population fail, given that the oyster fishery was, in theory at least, closely regulated? (Though we knew from Dave that massive amounts of cheating went on.)

The Solent was awash with excuses but no one was willing or brave enough to identify what had dealt the killer blow. A sort of myth had grown up among commercial oystermen, most of whom had devoted the past 50 years to growing the faster growing and introduced Pacific oyster, *Crassostrea gigas*, that the native oyster just wanted to die. There were so many things stacked against it, such as the parasite-borne disease bonamiosis which struck in the 1980s. Then there was predation from tingles, competition from slipper limpets and the introduction of the anti-fouling substance painted on boats, tributyltin. There might be competition with the Pacific oyster and the Manila clam, also present, though evidence did suggest the natives picked a different level of the shoreline to settle on. But the closer you looked, and the more you considered the plight of the Solent oyster against a global and historical perspective, taking into account the latest evidence, it seemed to us that the principal problem facing the oyster everywhere was simply over-exploitation.

This context was vital to our plan as without focusing on the principal problem, how to put masses of oysters back to improve the odds, we would be beating our heads against a wall. In his book *The Big Oyster*,[2] Mark Kurlansky tells the story of the enormous oyster beds which New York harbour, the Hudson River and Long Island Sound were known for up right until the twentieth century. The majority were wiped out by eighteenth- and nineteenth-century over-harvesting and then by pollution – and then New Yorkers just forgot about the natural profusion for which their city was once known. The remarkable Philine zu Ermgassen – who has taught me more about oysters than anyone else – and Brady Blake of the Washington State Department of Fish and Wildlife have documented how the Olympia oyster of the Pacific coast of the United States was wiped out by the 1920s in one of its strongholds in Willapa Bay, Washington state,[3] as it was in many locations on the Pacific coast. It was replaced, as elsewhere, by our old friend the Pacific oyster, *Crassostrea gigas*, which grew faster. In Australia, some 900 miles of coastline where reefs of the native Antipodean oyster *Ostrea angasi* were recorded at the time of colonisation had been entirely denuded of oysters by 1946.[4] Taken together with the systematic destruction of the great North Sea oyster fishery,[5] the evidence of overfishing seemed universal and the dominant factor in the oyster's demise.

The reality is that oysters need refuges where a core population can renew itself and re-seed other waters without being disturbed or harvested. The real game-changer, and one of the things that persuaded us to enter into partnership with Rob Clark and the Southern IFCA, was the creation of marine protected areas – places which the conservation rules said could not be dredged – all along the shores of the Solent. These had been appearing for various reasons over the past 20 years to the extent that by now they included most of the inshore. This would mean we could put broodstock oysters in permanent refuges where nobody could get at them. The best refuges would be as far west as possible because the currents flow from west to east. This meant the Beaulieu River, the Hamble and Newtown Creek on the Isle of Wight. But it was also worth concentrating on harbours, such as Langstone Harbour, the place where wild populations had been caught most recently. In Langstone, hydrologists had shown that the larvae tended to stay in the area instead of being carried out into the wider Solent. The hope was that if you put enough oysters back into all of these places and provided there was enough 'cultch', as old shells and gravel are known, for them to land on, there would eventually be a huge settlement of spat and the whole system would start working again. It was, we and our friends at the University of Portsmouth decided, a numbers game. We had to reintroduce enough oysters to overwhelm their enemies. It was a bit like Space Invaders.

Another vital thing that had moved things in our favour, we decided, was that Rob and the IFCA had managed to introduce a bylaw that allowed oyster fisheries to be closed, if necessary, according to more sensible criteria than those which had previously stopped him closing them until they were fished out. There was still a danger that a less far-sighted IFCA committee would one day lift the ban on dredging for oysters and the whole tragedy of the commons would start again. Though for now, at least, we had refuges and a better law. But how would we conquer the problem that there had been so few oysters dying off naturally in the Solent that there were too few old shells sitting on the surface of the mud, enough cultch, for the oyster spat to latch on to? And, what's more, how were we to find enough wild native oysters to achieve our reintroduction?

With Rob's encouragement, Tim Glover and I convened a group of local fishermen and experts to discuss whether oyster reintroduction was possible. After our first meeting, one night after work in Portsmouth, a local fisherman hung back in the shadows until all his colleagues had left. Then he said: 'If you don't do this, that will be it. The Solent will be a disaster.' Then he walked out into the night. Hope was evidently in short supply in those parts. A contact of ours told us, not entirely flippantly, that in the Solent, we were taking on the environmental equivalent of Syria, then at the height of its bloody civil war. We thought hard and took the view that we were working in enough pleasant blue-water places overseas and it was time we tried to achieve something good at home.

The Solent was a basket case but we were convinced it was not too late. Someone just needed to step in and reset the ambition, say how things could be and galvanise the community support which was evidently there. That was the other big thing that we had going for us: everyone we spoke to was in favour of bringing back the native oyster. We would provide the IFCA with the funds and the confidence to act above and beyond their government-determined budgets. They, in turn, would bring the legitimacy and law-making powers to defend any restoration we managed to achieve.

As I sat at my desk late one night at the very beginning, trying to write a vision of what we intended to do, I took consolation from the fact that people across the Atlantic were trying to rewild a place even more polluted and further from its pristine state – New York Harbour, the Hudson River and Long Island Sound. I read that conservationists had persisted even though the oysters they nurtured were unlikely ever to be fit for human consumption, just because of the ecological benefits they brought and because they were meant to be there. The level of contamination from industrial chemicals dumped there when the harbour was to all intents and purposes dead was just too high to expect the oysters to be safe to eat. That year, New York's Billion Oyster Project had been founded by Murray Fisher and Pete Malinowski. They claimed to have 10,000 volunteers and had solved the problem of there being no oyster shells for the oyster spat to land on by recycling oyster shells of any kind from restaurants all over Manhattan. There was no project in Europe yet in operation on such a scale, though we understood Dutch scientists had written a feasibility study about re-seeding the lost oyster beds of the Dutch part of the North Sea.

I could see that the scope of the oyster restoration projects in New York and Chesapeake Bay was dauntingly huge, with budgets to match, and the likelihood of success quite hard to estimate. But no one could knock the ambition. I felt we should have some of that in Europe, for if we didn't what hope was there of bringing back some measure of wildness to our heavily altered seas? Would funders back us, though, as we had only the vaguest idea of how to answer the questions 'when?' and 'how?'? British funders did indeed seem daunted by how expensive the project was likely to be.

Then one day in the depths of August, I received a call from someone who sat on the board of the US National Fish and

Wildlife Foundation, a statutory body that receives income from fines levied by US courts against companies that pollute the environment. He asked if I knew of anyone with a large-scale coastal restoration project around the UK coastline that needed funds. He could not find anything on the right scale. I asked why he was asking. He said a cruise ship had been fined several million dollars for oil pollution in US waters and a judge had ruled that a proportion of the fine should be given back to the UK, since it was the UK Marine and Coastguard Agency that had tipped off the US authorities that the ship was not compliant with environmental law. How much was the fine, I asked? 'The portion that has to come to the UK is a million dollars,' he replied. I felt that our ambition might at last be fulfilled. As so often before, the lesson was: dream big, build it and they will come.

The US experts at NFWF – known to everyone as Nifwif – knew all about oyster restoration, in fact more than we did. They had been funding restoration for years up and down the Atlantic and Gulf coasts. They listened, they asked questions and were not fazed when we said we did not know all the answers. They quietly enthused and gave us confidence that the British might attempt to emulate what the US had already successfully done around Chesapeake Bay. They kept us on the right tracks and have continued to be realistic and adaptable ever since. And boy, did we need to adapt. For the three greatest challenges for any oyster restoration project are to find enough oysters to re-stock, to find enough hard substrate for them to land on and to make sure that the majority of them do not die, which they are prone to do.

We had promised blithely that we would lay a million mature

oysters and enough material, whether recycled shells or gravel, for the oysters to fix themselves to. We then realised that the promises we'd received from native oyster breeders when it came to the volume of mature oysters they could supply were optimistic at best. Few of the hundreds of thousands of juvenile native oysters that we ordered from some of the few remaining companies who cultivated the native oyster, alongside the Pacific one, ever showed up. Faraway places such as Shetland, where they still bred a few natives, said they could supply them but then they were prevented from doing so by regulations about moving oysters designed to prevent disease.

A lot of soul-searching went on. Tim even discussed reopening the spatting ponds that existed in the nineteenth century beside the now derelict Fawley power station. Running a spatting pond ourselves, we decided, was too risky. The skills were lost. In the end, we decided to spend Nifwif's money – with their agreement – on a state-of-the-art hatchery at the University of Portsmouth with the target of producing a million oysters, spatted onto shell for maximum survivability, to be laid in the Solent. The hatchery at Southsea is now built and cultivating algae in parallel to feed to the oysters as they mature. We needed to ensure that the oysters used in the hatchery were sourced from the small remnant populations of the harbours around the Solent and the Isle of Wight – if we could find them – as after 40 years' exposure to the cruel disease of bonamiosis they evidently had some resistance. Otherwise, we would be creating a biological bomb that would tick for a while and then explode all of our achievements to date.

We were still short of mature broodstock – to be introduced to the seabed directly to double our chances of success. And we lacked, crucially, something to lay it on and to attract larvae that was produced by our caged oysters. We had tried introducing mature oysters without hard substrate in the Hamble and it had not worked so well; the oysters were washed away. I had a long chat with Jacob Kean Hammerson, then our Solent project officer, just as we had reached what felt like a tipping point. After long delays partly caused by the Covid pandemic, Jacob had secured a licence from the Marine Management Organisation to lay the cultch in the form of gravel and sanitised shell on the seabed in a determined area of Langstone Harbour. (This licence, incidentally, cost £12,000: why charities should have to pay to carry out work that meets government conservation targets is an issue I find mystifying.)

Oyster restoration was about to happen on an industrial scale for the first time. The timing, though, was critical. After eight months waiting for the licence – government agencies aren't in a hurry to do conservation or particularly attuned to the seasons – it was now July and Jacob was excitedly ordering up enormous red barges to deposit 500 tonnes of gravel and cockle shell in this carefully chosen section of Langstone Harbour. We purchased another 500 tons of gravel and shell to be deployed in the Hamble and Newtown Creek.

The idea was that we would source 100,000 mature oysters from a handful of native oyster producers in Scotland to balance out the much younger age profile of spat-on-shell oysters we would be receiving from the hatchery. A varied age structure would ensure more consistent spawning year by year. But after a cold spring, which would have been ideal for laying them, temperatures in the Solent were climbing. After fraught discussions our team decided to leave the oysters in cool Scottish water until temperatures cooled down a bit.

Then, in September, when Jacob had departed, something rather wonderful happened. Our team, marshalled by Morven Robertson, pulled together the fraying loose ends that had not come together in the summer. It began to look and feel like a military operation, which is what it needed to be. Huge red barges, filmed by drones from the air, began laying out vast amounts of gravel in Langstone Harbour, under the critical eyes of our man, Luke, and his former supervisor, Dr Joanne Preston from the University of Portsmouth, who had developed the oyster hatchery.

At this point, Luke and Jenny, a new recruit, went to Scotland – only to find rather fewer oysters than they were expecting for there had been some mortality over the summer. There were 15,000 natives lying in Loch Linnhe. They had to extract them by hand and immediately drive them south, an exacting task. The oysters arrived in baskets and there was a call for volunteers to help with biosecurity checks – this involved removing other species, such as mussels and tube worms, extracting any mortalities and bathing the rest in bleach to kill off any remaining hitch-hikers. The surviving oysters were allowed to recover over the weekend. The Monday the mature oysters were to be dropped on top of the cultch was due to be stormy but the front was forecast to clear around 11. We had our weather window and tipped off the BBC's *One Show*, which had been waiting for months to record the event.

When I arrived at the boat with Jo and Luke, I realised the fisherman at the helm looked familiar. It was Chris Breeze, based in Gosport, who had come to our very first meeting in Portsmouth to discuss the Solent seven years earlier. Chris had fished for the native oyster for 20 years up until the closure. It was very lucrative, he said. (No wonder the fishermen fought hard not to give it up.) But then the end came, the licences were withdrawn. Chris's theory was that the oysters were overwhelmed by their predators, such as the tingles, which drill into the shell. Chris had told Jo, at the beginning of our project, that her idea of oyster hotels would not work, yet he now conceded that there was evidence of spat from the larval burst the oysters in the marinas had produced around the shore of Langstone Harbour. We were now laying gravel on top of the slipper limpets, which ought to knock them out for a bit. This was our first large-scale laying of cultch as well as oysters, and the first, military-scale boost to the system, on the scale Jo, Luke and Tim had seen done on the US east coast.

Luke, the scientist, laid out his baskets of oysters neatly on the raised deck of Chris's boat, the *Castanet*. When the GPS said we had reached the rectangular boundary of the area where the cultch had been laid, he began pushing the oysters off into the turbid water with a metal ruler. Others took turns and were less precise but the oysters all went over the side. Jo said that they had tried pouring them down tubes but had found that the oysters just landed on top of each other, so sowing them like seed was the better way for them to disperse. You could see them as they fluttered down, we hoped to land on the hard substrate. Next summer, as temperatures rose, with luck they would spawn. I selected five oysters and pushed them over the side myself. It felt like dropping coins into a fountain. What were the chances our wishes would come true?

Chris, who had moved on to Manila clams and, a new arrival in the harbour, scallops, was still sceptical that we could re-seed the whole Solent with oysters, but he believed, encouragingly, we could succeed in enclosed harbours, such as Langstone. Jo Preston and I took a more strategic view of the operation. We hoped that the process of laying so many oysters on so much cultch would start a huge pulse of larvae and that by the end of all our efforts, in a few years, the Solent would be larval soup, just as the North Sea must have been when it had oyster beds 200 miles long. Next spring, we would lay another 20,000 oysters in Langstone Harbour. Then we would move on to lay a new reef in the Hamble before natural spawning started.

We had begun the journey in the Solent and on a smaller scale in the Blackwater Estuary in Essex, where more native oysters survived to provide the broodstock, in partnership with the Blackwater oystermen, who have more of a tradition of mariculture than just extraction, as in the Solent. Across the country, we now have a native oyster network egging each other on and across Europe, since 2017, the scientific legions have been gathering and pooling resources under the Native Oyster Restoration Alliance.

Whenever you look for oysters, you tend to find remnants hanging on, waiting for conditions to improve: a big oyster story that autumn was the discovery of a reef of 100,000 oysters nobody knew was there in Rotterdam Harbour. For us, at last, there was a sense of momentum which meant individual projects would be carried along and have support. There were now other coalition partners suspending oysters beneath pontoons in the Firth of Clyde, Conway Bay and Tyne and Wear. We had also begun to look at restoring salt marsh and seagrass meadows in conjunction with oyster reefs because evidence showed the combination seemed to work even better. The Portsmouth hatchery, which had managed to get impressive spawning of larvae from its broodstock oysters, now had to perfect feeding them with algae long enough for them to form spat which would then attach itself to the sterilised oyster shells collected for the purpose. There was still a lot of work to do but the momentum had begun to feel unstoppable.

I asked Rob Clark, by then in a different role, whether he believed the seeding of the Solent was going to work, provided we put in the amount of oysters we planned. 'Yes,' he said, 'but over a long time-frame.' We now had the refuges, we would eventually have enough oysters and we had a Solent community that was discussing and understanding the problems in a more rounded way. We had plenty of time to work out how oyster fishing would be regulated when there were enough oysters for dredging to resume: Rob said we should be prepared for a 20-year wait. We were invested and tooled up for the task ahead. The next bit was down to the fickle flat oyster, which no doubt had a few surprises in store. We had taken on one of the biggest rewilding schemes in Europe. By boosting the oyster population and reviving one of the Solent's keystone species, our experiment could have the power to bring back not just oysters but so many other de-wilded marine creatures, too. If that wasn't daunting enough, while all this had been going on, we had been pursuing even larger opportunities for rewilding in the United Kingdom's Overseas Territories.

5

Jurassic Parks of the Sea

'I am convinced that only by setting aside half the planet in reserve, or more, can we save the living part of the environment and achieve the stabilization required for our own survival.'

Edward O. Wilson, *Half-Earth: Our Planet's Fight for Life*,
Liveright Publishing Corp, 2016

'It hath certain faire and white Sandes about it, and great store of Fish, wherein it surpasseth S. Helena, but in it there are no beastes at all, onely by reason of the great quantitie of Fishes ther are so many birds in it yt.'

Jan Huyghen van Linschoten, merchant and historian, 1596

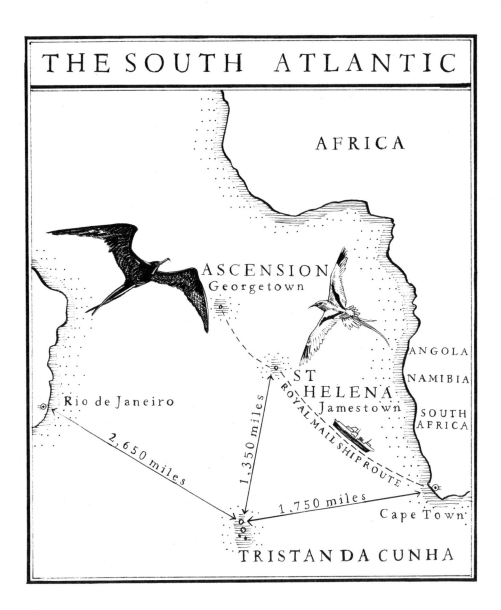

THE SOUTH ATLANTIC

AFRICA

ASCENSION
Georgetown

ST
HELENA
Jamestown

ANGOLA

NAMIBIA

SOUTH
AFRICA

Rio de Janeiro

ROYAL MAIL SHIP ROUTE

1,350 miles

2,650 miles

1,750 miles

Cape Town

TRISTAN DA CUNHA

A scension Island, in the middle of the tropical Atlantic, is one of the most bizarre and exciting places I have ever visited. On the one occasion I approached the island from the sea, flying fish leaped from the bow-wave of the ship. Between us and land was the arc of a single, leaping hammerhead shark. The volcanic terrain consists of dusty red hills and baking hot black lava flows around a large green mountain topped by a forest, its peak frequently in cloud. At sea level it is equatorially hot. When we were ferried ashore, the island's own endemic frigatebird, an uncannily pterodactyl-like creature, flew low over the boat with an eye out for something to eat, which you got the feeling in more distressed circumstances might have been us. Looking down, as the launch reached dry land by a pier and some harbour buildings that date from just after the Napoleonic wars, we noticed the shoals of black trigger fish on the surface, also looking for food. Trigger fish can nibble you if they get excited and there is food about but they are not as large or as aggressive as some of the inhabitants of Ascension's waters.

Ascension is one of the 14 British Overseas Territories, specks scattered across the oceans of the world, not quite large enough to be countries in their own right. For historical reasons, the UK has the fifth-largest exclusive economic zone in the world, but because of the distribution of its territories across every ocean except the Arctic, these waters are among the most diverse on Earth. They were once memorably, and accurately, described as 'fragments of paradise'.[1] They contain 94 per cent of the UK's unique biodiversity, a massive proportion of its natural riches, so they are, frankly, a huge responsibility. Though the islands are mostly small, each island, or island group, lays claim to many thousands of square miles of ocean within its exclusive economic zone, thanks to the UN Law of the Sea, which says that each inhabited land mass owns rights to its sea for 200 nautical miles all around. So it is not surprising that those of us intending to make sure governments follow through on their promises to protect 10 per cent of the ocean's total area by 2020[2] became preoccupied with the UK Overseas Territories. Three of these, Tristan da Cunha, St Helena and Ascension, all with their own separate administrations, count as one territory as they are under one governor, a UK government official, though they are hundreds of miles apart and spread across the South Atlantic. One of these, Ascension had no commercial fishing fleet, so it looked as though it might be the most open-minded to the case for protection.

At the beginning of the century, the amount of the world's ocean protected for its wildlife was 0.7 per cent. By the time I first went to Ascension in October 2015, Chagos, also a UK Overseas Territory, had become the world's largest no-take marine protected area, nearly doubling that total. South Georgia, another UKOT which has been described as the Galápagos of the South Atlantic for its astonishing abundance of wildlife including a recovering population of whales, seals and penguins, had been protected by the South Georgia government (which, the island being largely uninhabited, really means the British government) under an agreement that permitted strictly controlled fishing for toothfish and krill in some designated areas, which in turn paid for enforcement.[3] The British government liked the idea of a mix of fishing and conservation in each territory but this concept was not to prove particularly helpful in resolving discussions in the other territories. All had local governments with some degree of independence from the UK – though this was weakest in the case of Ascension, strongest in the Falklands and the Caribbean. The question, after the declaration of the big reserve in the Chagos, was which of the other UK Overseas Territories could be persuaded to have marine protected areas and which would set their face against it. In the end, Ascension, St Helena and Tristan – and Pitcairn in the Pacific – all took on protected areas of different kinds for different reasons. All made decisions of their own but needed encouragement, advice and funding from outside. In each case, except Pitcairn, there was a degree of threat – fishing operations catching sensitive and endangered species – that drove the case for protection along.

Ascension Island has a very distinct character from St Helena, its sister island 700 miles away, where two thirds of its working residents, the 'Saints', come from. Looking up from the shore, the eye is drawn to the extraordinary number of aerials and satellite dishes on the lava flows and low hills. Ascension is a tracking station for satellites and the BBC beams out its World Service transmissions from there to Africa, 1,000 miles away across the Atlantic. It is also a kind of mothballed staging post for the RAF and United States Air Force, both of which have bases there. The island's long runway was first built in the Second World War, when upwards of 25,000 aircraft supplied by the US used the island as a stepping-stone on their way to North Africa and southern Europe. Ascension served as a base for the Avro Vulcan bombers and Victor tanker aircraft which destroyed the runway at Port Stanley in the Falklands war. Its present massive runway – currently waiting for a huge crack caused by water running through it to be repaired – was built as an alternative landing strip for the Space Shuttle. There is still a fly-boy culture on Ascension, a bit of Tom Wolfe's *The Right Stuff* in the bars and messes, which comes from its continued association with space and aviation. The T-shirt they sell in the island's museum says 'Windshear free since 1943' – a dig aimed at neighbouring St Helena's windshear-troubled new runway. St Helena has had its revenge because the Voyager aircraft which form the 'air bridge' from RAF Brize Norton to the Falklands, which used to refuel here, cannot use Ascension's runway until the crack is repaired. Until it is, the only way in and out, for Brits anyway (the US C-17 aircraft do not require such a long runway), is via the much-ridiculed runway in St Helena.

Part of the culture too is showing visitors some of the wildlife spectaculars that Ascension can lay on. Ascension's crabs live on the land, not in the sea. Catch the right time of year and you will see bright yellow and orange crabs migrating slowly from their burrows on Green Mountain down to the surf. They run onto the wet sand as the waves recede and lay their eggs with a little wriggle and then instantly scuttle back before the next wave comes because they cannot swim. Hundreds of thousands of sooty or 'wideawake' terns leave their single eggs on the ground in nesting season to wheel and cry overhead as one makes the pilgrimage to the salt-water ponds where the island's two very small, endemic shrimps are to be found, together with a black and white, zebra-marked eel.

More spectacular still is the arrival of the vast green turtles which haul themselves up the steep sand beaches to dig their nests and lay their eggs at night, so the frigatebirds cannot eat them. Then, exhausted, these diligent, enormous mothers claw their way back to the waves in the light of dawn, suddenly becoming graceful sea creatures again as they reach the surf, achieve floatation and their powerful flippers carry them away. The green turtles have been a conservation success story since people stopped eating them: now their population is rising. Ascension is the green turtles' second largest egg-laying ground in the Atlantic Ocean. The turtle ponds where sailing ships used to pick up a few turtles as meat for sailors are still there by the harbour, though like most of the historic buildings on Ascension they are in poor repair.

The turtles are by no means the largest creatures in what Colin Chester, proprietor of a sport fishing company that used to work on Ascension, described to me as a 'Jurassic Park of the sea'. You have only to look at the photographs on the wall of the Obsidian, the island's only hotel, to see an array of the island's megafauna: 1,000lb-plus blue marlin, black marlin, sailfish, yellowfin tuna and wahoo, and with them in the photographs the grinning trophy hunters who had caught them. There were two sport fishing companies working before the long runway closed. Their clients were usually rich, like the party of New York bond dealers I met with huge traditional game rods and reels. Spear fishing was also popular, both among the residents of the US Air Force base and fortunate outsiders who got to visit. A member of the Qatari royal family flew in with an entourage of 60, equipped with their own beds, to spear fish for tuna for a month.

By no means all of those who came to fish for sport were privileged; some were just ingenious. I met Adam 'Epi' Epifanis, a working-class Australian of Greek origin who specialised in fishing from the shore with rod and line in his native land. He had persuaded a fishing tackle company to sponsor his specimen-hunting trip as the ultimate test of its fishing gear. This it duly received. We met after he had claimed the world record for a yellowfin tuna caught from the shore. He bettered this within three days with one of 257lbs. (Though the larger fish would have weighed a bit more if a shark hadn't taken a chunk out of it as it was coming to shore.) Epi's battle with those yellowfin, which the rules dictated he had to haul ashore alone on the razor-sharp volcanic rocks, eventually went up on YouTube. The day of his second triumph, he had to be patched up and his bleeding wounds treated with iodine by a concerned member of the hotel staff. Epi was tough. He knew what he wanted and he landed the fish that made his name.

Fishing with rod and line is one of the perks for the residents of Ascension and a steak of fresh yellowfin or wahoo is a way of varying the usual diet of flown-in and canned food. This wouldn't be Jurassic Park, though, without a faint sense that the human predators are also on the menu. That feeling made its return with the sudden arrival inshore, after several years of absence, of muscular Galápagos sharks. They were first seen at night down by the pier, near the table where the fish are gutted. They had slack, empty flanks. They were hungry. Shortly after, I went out fishing for the pot with Patrick, a 'Saint' from St Helena, who worked at the air base. I hooked what Patrick estimated was a 50lb tuna, which nearly pulled the rod out of my unaccustomed hands on its first run. Then there were three huge thumps on the end of the line, which suddenly went slack. The hook came up baitless. The yellowfin had been eaten off it by sharks. They surfaced and gave our boat a cursory bump or two to see if they could hole it and tip us into the water. I figured that Epi was lucky to get his giant fish out of the sea. The sharks, which were around 2.5 metres long, became a problem for those used to enjoying the balmy temperatures of Ascension's two or three bathing beaches. Two shark attacks, one serious, caused understandable alarm and led to calls for a cull, which might or might not have been practicable or done any good. Swimming and diving were then banned, until the Galápagos sharks had vanished again.

The ban on swimming, while it lasted, was a shame for residents and visitors alike. There is so much to see by snorkelling or diving in Ascension's waters, which I have done, swimming alongside turtles in Comfortless Cove or above juvenile hammerheads around Boatswain Bird Island. In the past decade, so much has been discovered about the island's marine life and what makes it special.[4] There are no big corals here, it is too young an island, but their niche is taken by coralline algae which looks like pink candyfloss and forms impressive towers. The fish are a mix of species from both sides of the Atlantic and the Caribbean. More fish species originated in the west than the east. There are moray eels and schools of jack and 11 species of fish found nowhere else. Ascension Island's endemic sea bream evolved from a species recognisably from Africa, the endemic angelfish from a visitor from Brazil. A further 20 fish species are found only here, in St Helena and in St Peter and Paul's Rocks, an archipelago under the sovereignty of Brazil. At night, Ascension's ubiquitous triggerfish charmingly drop to the seabed asleep, like falling leaves. It is a bizarre place but special, too.

Why do we now think Ascension is so important, other than for the impressive array of creatures that can be seen on the island and in its immediate coastal waters? Because although it is right in the middle of the most-fished part of the tropical Atlantic, I don't think it is too fanciful to say that it is an insurance policy that could rewild the entire ocean one day if there is a catastrophe which affects marine animals – which is looking likely, if their declines go on as they are. It is one of the places which could help reverse the species extinction crisis and ensure the long-term health of our planet – as the great naturalist and 'father of biodiversity', Edward O. Wilson, has urged. How do we know that? From many studies but one in particular.

The island's remoteness – it is some 1,000 miles from the coast of Africa and 1,400 miles from the coast of Brazil – does not wholly explain why it is a Jurassic Park for big fish, most of which are supposed to be highly migratory. An insight was gained by the late Kate Downes, who worked for the island's Conservation Department before she died tragically young from a brain tumour. She studied the yellowfin tuna that were landed and found that these creatures that had been confidently assumed by fisheries scientists to range ceaselessly across the oceans, were in fact resident in Ascension waters for more than 200 days a year. This explained their high average size and the fact that they had not been caught by the longline fleets which lay their 80-mile baited lines 200 miles off the island, out beyond the borders of Ascension's exclusive fishing zone. The tuna were doing what they had probably always done, gathering around the island itself, in its rich waters and its mini-upwelling which brings nutrients to the surface and feeds other, smaller species, but it was intriguing to speculate whether the more naturally residential tuna in other places worldwide had all been caught and these were some of the only sedentary ones that remained.

Like many remote islands, Ascension's ecology bears the scars of catastrophic human interventions but also shows the results of some conservation triumphs. Around the island, the guano deposits on now-uninhabited rocks speak of a population of birds many times larger than it is today. Darwin, who visited the island on the *Beagle* in 1836, blamed the loss of birds on a plague of introduced cats and rats. Only one of the 11 breeding seabirds presently found on Ascension, the wideawake tern, survived on the mainland until the beginning of this century. Mercifully, the cats and rats were brought under control in the early 2000s – thanks to a collaboration between the island's government and the Royal Society for the Protection of Birds – and the birds are back breeding on the mainland, even the frigatebird whose whole world population was once pushed back to the rocky outcrop called Boatswain Bird Island. Now the frigatebirds nest on remote rocky eminences around the main island itself, which is a triumph for the island and its Conservation Department.

We needed evidence of the incredible fecundity of the island's waters to make the case for protection both to the residents themselves and people back home. The records of what had happened to Ascension's waters were poor, so I roughed out a study I would like to see done, based on both historical records and the memories of older people who had worked on the island or who still did, which was to be called 'old men and the sea'. This was taken on by a researcher called Polly Burns, who did an astonishingly thorough study involving interviews with 130 present and past Ascension residents. Her report concluded that Ascension 'has immense conservation importance as a rare survival of prolific marine life in an ocean more often characterised by declines'. She even found something out about the Galápagos sharks, a species which in turn both scared and annoyed Ascension residents. Historically, she found there were periods when the sharks went away and times when they came back with a vengeance, in the mid-nineteenth and early twentieth centuries, and again after the war. Swimming in the sea was banned then, too. It may not have been much consolation but it banished the sense that something unfamiliar was happening.

However, even though Ascension doesn't have its own fishing fleet, its marine life, and particularly its big fish, were under threat. The British government keep the island very short of cash and the appointed administrator and the elected councillors had taken to selling licences to foreign fleets, with no supervision of what they caught. In 2011, the peak year of selling licences, the island earned more than £1 million from Taiwan, Japan, the Philippines and Belize. Some 2,601 tonnes of tuna were reported caught and some 261 tonnes of bycatch landed, which included blue marlin, black and striped marlin, sailfish and blue sharks. Blue marlin is 'vulnerable', according to the IUCN Red List of Endangered Species, and blue shark is 'near threatened', so this alone was a cause for concern. Given that the British government was fond of boasting that it had created two of the largest marine protected areas in the world, Chagos and South Georgia, the latter with a 'gold standard' of satellite monitoring and enforcement, this lucrative but wholly unmonitored plunder of some of the species that made Ascension special looked increasingly irresponsible and out-of-date.

The catch volumes reported looked suspiciously low relative to the 65 vessels which had been fishing – indicating that the reported figures may not have been telling the whole story. I discovered what had been going on in a previous period, five years or so earlier, from Stedson Stroud, who was, at the time of my first visit, the manager of the national park on the top of Green Mountain. Stedson was an experienced sailor who had travelled far up and down the Atlantic in the Merchant Navy and on the Royal Mail Ship *St Helena*. He had visited South Georgia and also Tristan da Cunha and its remote islands of Inaccessible, Gough and Nightingale, with their enormous colonies of albatross, shearwater and rockhopper penguins. Throughout the 11 years he sailed the Atlantic, he said you knew when you were near Ascension because you encountered vessels with shark fins hung out to dry on washing lines. In 2005, the captain of a Taiwanese longliner fishing in Ascension waters transmitted a distress call and asked to put ashore. The vessel was allowed to land on the condition that it was inspected. Along with the expected freezer cabinets containing tuna, inspectors found in excess of 1,000 sharks' fins. So it looks as if the old practice of shark finning may have been going on which kept the catch tonnages low as the sharks' bodies would have been pushed over the side, alive, to die in the sea. That's not all. In 2010, Stedson was on a voyage commissioned by the Foreign Office which found that there were higher levels of illegal fishing around Ascension than any of the other South Atlantic territories.

It has been estimated that a million sharks are killed for their fins each year in the ocean,[5] which has resulted in most shark species ending up on the Red List of Endangered Species and, crucially, removed from their important ecosystem function. Killing sharks is one of the clearest examples of 'de-wilding' the ocean, in which human greed has nearly killed off entire species, destabilising whole ecosystems in the process.

Some time before I came on the scene, another conservationist spotted the de-wilding that was diminishing the value of this extraordinary and remote place. Jonathan Hall, from the RSPB, my friend and colleague in the Marine Reserves Coalition, challenged Ascension Island's administrator, Colin Wells, over it single-handedly in a series of letters. Wells imposed a moratorium on the sale of fishing licences in 2013 pending a review into how vessels should be regulated and their catch accurately recorded. Hall had already been to see Wells in his residence on Green Mountain, where he was told that the revenue of licences was vital to the island's economy and the RSPB had better drop the idea of Ascension's waters ever becoming a marine reserve. That, said Wells, was not going to happen.

Hall now had a campaign on his hands, so he sought our help. Ascension actually had many things going for it as a marine reserve. It had its extraordinary ecology, more about which was being discovered year on year. As it had no resident commercial fishing fleet, most of the people on the island (of whom there were around 800) tended to look on its surroundings with the same wonder and interest that we did, but they were vulnerable to the idea of selling licences for revenue-raising to cover the island's expenditure, if the commercial fishing was out of sight and out of mind. Each of the Overseas Territories has a degree of self-determination, yet because of its tiny population and its military uses, Ascension was more influenced by London than the other islands. Its occupants seemed the most sympathetic of all the Overseas Territories if protecting their waters, and potentially restoring those few species that had already been over-exploited, was your game. And London might just be persuaded to overrule the views of its administrator, who would, in any case, not be there forever.

The RSPB demolished the economic case being made by some of the islanders for selling licences by publishing a report which pointed out that the true costs of managing a sustainable fishery for tuna as done in South Georgia would be significantly more than £400,000 a year. The income from selling licences had averaged only £700,000 a year even in the most lucrative of years, so it was clear that a properly run, properly enforced fishery would be marginal in terms of economic returns. As a result, we got indications from friendly councillors that they would be happy with licensing fishing on only half of their waters while making the rest – an area nearly as big as the UK – into a reserve. This was a great compromise between the various interests on the island and gave us much encouragement. But there were understandable differences between the councillors over how much to ask the British government for in return. All were rightly adamant that the British government should pick up the tab for enforcing and monitoring the reserve and that the cost should not fall on a population of 800 people. But what else to ask for in return for giving up a potential income in perpetuity?

The islanders knew how little the British government spent on the island's infrastructure – virtually nothing. We had seen the school, the children's swimming pool, the semi-derelict Exiles Club – a magnificent Georgian building, once the marine barracks – and other historic buildings, all in poor repair. A couple of years later, the island's only petrol station was found to be unsafe and a senior official fell into the sewage plant and had to be rescued when its surrounding wall collapsed. There was also the biggest political issue of all on Ascension, the 'right of abode': the ability to buy land and property, which residents are not allowed to do. Everything belongs to the Ascension Island government and residents must leave if they retire or reach 18 and do not have a job. The UK government had considered giving the islanders the right of abode in 2006 and thought better of it.

One potential obstacle in the way of our plans to make the waters around Ascension Island a marine park was in fact friendly fire, of a sort. The wealthy American NGO the Pew Charitable Trusts was lobbying our government, taking up a lot its attention, to protect the waters of the Pitcairn Islands in the Pacific, one of the last marine wildernesses on Earth, instead. Could it come down to them or us? However, there was another way of looking at it. The addition to the campaign for Pitcairn of an urgent campaign to conserve Ascension could strengthen the case for protection of these hugely significant ecosystems, winning the government's support together.

This was a turning point at which we realised that what we were really campaigning for were marine reserves – or the nearest thing to full protection that was politically feasible and practical – around all 14 of the UK Overseas Territories. Some of the populations of those territories, such as the Falklands, were less immediately receptive to the idea, so that message needed to be finessed – we couldn't go against the wishes of the islanders. But that is what it was. We needed to find a way of getting our demands into the political parties' manifestos for the 2015 general election. For now, we decided to campaign explicitly for Pitcairn, Ascension and a fully protected or no-take reserve around the uninhabited South Sandwich Islands between South Georgia and the Antarctic peninsula.

To get our campaign on the government's radar, the parliamentary champion of our coalition, Zac Goldsmith MP, agreed to publish a pamphlet on Ascension, Pitcairn and South Georgia in autumn 2014. Then BLUE's co-founder, Chris Gorell Barnes, secured a meeting with Jo Johnson, head of Prime Minister David Cameron's Number 10 policy unit, who was looking for 'green' policies for the manifesto. He sounded keen and asked us to make a presentation to the man with the power to make it happen: Cameron's 'fixer' and the head of the Cabinet Office, Oliver Letwin. This our coalition did just before Christmas 2014.

All went quiet until a reception in the House of Commons in February that was to be a public appeal for our proposals to be included in the party manifestos – and the launch of our alliance's new name, the Great British Oceans coalition. On the day, we managed to place several striking pictures[6] of the actor Helena Bonham Carter embracing a yellowfin tuna – found in the waters of both Ascension and Pitcairn – on the front page and page three of the London *Evening Standard*. Paul Rose, an expedition leader from *National Geographic*'s non-profit Pristine Seas, spoke on behalf of

Pitcairn. Sylvia Earle, the distinguished American marine conservationist who had just journeyed to the island at our request, spoke on behalf of Ascension. Jonathan Hall, who accompanied her on her trip, told me privately that he had a written understanding from the Ascension Island council in his pocket that they would consider a marine protected area if the UK government finance was agreed. This was duly sent through to Oliver Letwin, who had asked for written confirmation that they were on board.

The government's annual budget a few days later contained an announcement. Chancellor George Osborne said it was the government's intention to go ahead with a reserve in the waters around the Pitcairn Islands. This would be the world's largest marine reserve at 322,138 square miles, an area three times the size of the UK and larger than California and Texas. We wondered what had happened to an announcement about Ascension. Gorell Barnes nudged Johnson by email. Johnson replied encouragingly, if cryptically: 'It's just the start . . . we're going to save all the fish everywhere!'

Just what that meant we had to wait until April, when the Conservative manifesto was published, to find out. It was clear that our policy had appealed to David Cameron. The manifesto said that a future Conservative government would create a 'Blue Belt' around all 14 UK Overseas Territories, 'subject to local support'. Cameron had added his own unexpected flourish by calling it the 'Blue Belt.'

Incredibly, our own idea had come drifting back to us on the political tide like a message in a bottle. We were stunned. Zac Goldsmith was jubilant. He and Nick Hurd, a like-minded MP, wrote an article calling it: 'The biggest conservation commitment by any government ever.' It was indeed a very big deal. The Great British Oceans coalition had turned out to be one of the most successful campaigning groups on record.

However, it doesn't take long for the shine to wear off in politics. That May, the Conservatives were returned as a majority government. Theoretically, that meant they now had to implement their manifesto commitment. In fact, when we finally got a meeting with Oliver Letwin on 8 June, World Oceans Day, it was a sombre affair. He explained to us that the party's commitment had yet to become the policy of the government. The British civil service had opposed the commitment at every turn and one permanent secretary had required a 'ministerial direction' so it could not be blamed on him or his staff if the Blue Belt turned out to be horrendously expensive, unworkable or unpopular. For the Blue Belt to be adopted as government policy, it needed a budget and a plan of implementation. It had neither.

We decided to raise some money as soon as possible. For the proposition to be sufficiently attractive to a big conservation funder, we thought at least 50 per cent of Ascension's waters would have to be a reserve (that would be an area nearly the size of the UK). This would also keep the government's ambitions high. The island council was still determined to restart the sale of fishing licences that September, so we didn't have long.

I rang our co-founder and ace fundraiser, George Duffield. George had been asking for a new Chagos-style project to fund for five years. He managed to find an established US conservation donor, Louis Bacon, whose son had been to Ascension with the US armed forces. He knew the place! Bacon summoned us to his hedge fund's eyrie in Mayfair one evening. He proposed to put up £200,000 a year for two years on the condition we got a reserve designated. I noticed he made his decision quickly, leaving his staff and advisers to catch up. George and I were delighted and impressed.

We still had to make sure this offer was acceptable to the UK government, and its super-reluctant civil service, and filled the gap of 18 months before the Treasury said it was prepared to fund the Blue Belt. Oliver Letwin was at the Conservative party conference when I telephoned him. He had a very specific deal in mind: we would pay £300,000, a third less than Bacon had offered, which would cover the hire of a patrol boat and other expenses. An extra £70,000 for satellite surveillance would be found elsewhere. It was a snip: it was one of the largest marine reserves in the Atlantic and an improbably small sum had got it over the line.

That was by no means the end of it, though. The Ascension Island councillors had to be happy and they, it turned out, didn't think the deal was enough. They had expected an element of compensation for income foregone. But Letwin had his deal with the Treasury and he was in no mood to brook delay. He instructed the governor to order the island to create the protected area. The councillors grumbled their hands had been forced but they were also, we heard, privately reassured that the British government would be picking up the tab.

A month later, I was on Ascension, meeting a new administrator, Marc Holland, and the fiercely bright head of fisheries and conservation, Dr Judith Brown. She poured scorn on my proposed deal, arguing that that she would prefer to see either zero or 100 per cent of Ascension's waters protected. Fifty per cent seemed to be based neither on science nor economics. This I knew perfectly well. It was based on politics. Fifty per cent was the most the Foreign Office would concede or the councillors would support, so having made her point, Jude began drawing up the boundaries of an area that looked like half an orange tilted to the right. I remember saying to Jude, 'Don't worry, we will campaign for the other 50 per cent of Ascension's waters. It may take us five years.' In the event it took three.

When fishing reopened in the area where it was still permitted, Jude spent a couple of months at sea on a fishing vessel, the *Extractor*, that she resourcefully commissioned from St Helena, inspecting the Taiwanese fishing vessels that bought licences. There turned out to be only 2, compared with the 20 that had been hoped for. Under the new, tougher rules, Ascension required inspections of boats and crew's equipment at sea. This revealed a lack of safety equipment, such as life jackets, and poor onboard living conditions for the crew. The new rules meant that no fishing vessels applied for licences in subsequent years, leaving a newly elected batch of Ascension councillors to conclude that they should throw in their lot with a 99.5 per cent reserve – the second largest no-take zone in the Atlantic – leaving a 12-mile zone around the island for recreational and subsistence fishing.

As I write, the councillors are still discussing proposed regulations for sport fishing which have been in train since 2002. At issue is how many of the spectacular beasts of the sea will be landed dead – ideally, only fish of record size – and how catch-and-release will be practised for the rest. I have every sympathy with the island's wish to preserve the trophy fishing for which it is rightly known and which brings in income from visiting anglers but the objective of marine protected areas is conservation. It is an uneasy balance to strike.

Three years after the first announcement of a reserve in Ascension and with a reserve about to be agreed for virtually the whole of Ascension's waters, we still felt that something was missing – rather as we had a few years earlier in Lyme Bay. We felt it was important to give the island's residents something they could point to as a lasting benefit from creating the reserve, their gift to the world. Otherwise, all they would have to keep them supporting a reserve in future was the reassurance that the seas around their shores were protected and more scientists would be turning up from time to time (science tourism, as it is called). There was also a need to fund a new development path no longer based on extraction but on eco-tourism – and whatever else the residents of the island felt they needed. To that end, my colleague Clare Brook at BLUE persuaded the visionary conservation donor, Peter Lürssen, the superyacht builder, to fund a £2 million endowment so that the island would always have sums of money for community projects that benefit the island and help it to develop eco-tourism, in recognition of the globally important step it had taken.

Looking back, we have come a long way. Without the campaign for Ascension, I don't believe there would have been a Blue Belt. Ascension's huge reserve in the middle of the most-fished part of the tropical Atlantic stands comparison with the American national parks or the great game reserves in Africa which became national parks, such as the Kruger. Ascension's combination of a recreational fishing core and a huge no-fishing, no-extraction area around it is of the islanders' choosing. The island has done things its own way. Its residents can feel proud. Meanwhile, in St Helena and Tristan da Cunha, things played out somewhat differently . . .

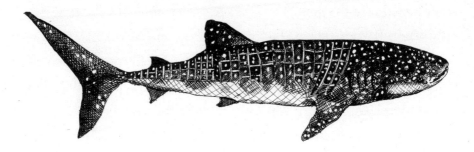

When the Royal Mail ship approached St Helena after five days at sea from Cape Town, the island loomed out of the dawn mist like a lost world. For several days now we had been without sight of ships, aircraft or even birds. The first sign that we were approaching this remote, isolated volcanic outcrop, like Ascension but older, at about 14 million years old, was the reappearance of petrels. The only other sign of life when nothing else was to be seen was something I had only ever read about. Leaping out from the bow wave in a display of perfect synchronised swimming was a shoal of hundreds of tiny flying squid, three or four inches long.

As daylight brought clarity, we remarked on its dark, forbidding cliffs and brown vegetation-less slopes on all sides facing the sea. We knew, though, that, unlike Ascension, St Helena has lush cattle pastures and woodland in its sheltered inland valleys, where entrancing fairy terns nest, balancing their single egg on a bough. But when the Portuguese discovered St Helena in 1502 they reported that its outer cliffs and slopes were emerald green with lush vegetation. They said it looked like paradise. It just lacked one thing: domestic animals from which passing ships might replenish their larders. So they introduced the goat. The goats had been culled by the time that Napoleon Bonaparte was famously exiled there in 1815 by the victors of Waterloo, with his staff of generals. At their most numerous, in the 1700s, the goat herds were said to be several miles long. The sea ran black with eroded soil. Gone are the soil and vegetation now, including most of the endemic plants, from most of St Helena's cliffs and mountainous slopes. This makes St Helena one of the best examples of how a single introduced species can prove catastrophic to an isolated island ecosystem. Its marine resources are less compromised, though. As we drew into Jamestown harbour the captain announced that six mature whale sharks could be seen from the bridge.

The whale sharks are one of the attractions most likely to draw outsiders to St Helena. They face no immediate threat in St Helena's waters but the IUCN Red List records them globally as endangered as their numbers are estimated to have declined by around half over the last 75 years. Most of those that turn up around February each year are mature specimens in roughly equal proportions male and female, strongly suggesting that they are gathering to mate, an act which local conservationists say they have witnessed. The mating of whale sharks has yet to be filmed anywhere in the world. Where the whale sharks go for the rest of the year or where they give birth no one knows. What is certain is that these massive filter feeders, known locally as 'bone sharks' due to their large bone-like dorsal ridges, turn up at St Helena at the time the skipjack tuna spawn, when the sea around the island is a soup of fish eggs. At other times, they will eat plankton, animal and vegetable, and even sardines and anchovies. But this time-honoured connection between the arrival of the gentle giants and timing of the tuna spawning is what gives a sense of utter fragility to the whole of St Helena's ecosystem, for tuna are also the main target species of the island's small commercial fishing fleet and a staple of the diet of this remote community. So far, subsistence, tourism and nature are in balance but it is not difficult to see how things could be otherwise.

What I did not realise, until I went snorkelling with whale sharks and Beth Taylor, who established the first marine conservation department at the St Helena National Trust, was just how close in to the island these huge sharks – which can grow to 12 metres – swim and how easy it is to see them. One glided serenely by between our boat and the cliffs, looking at first like a mat of green seaweed the size of a bus. The whale shark, a relatively young one I was told, turned out of curiosity and came to look at us, just after we slipped into the water with our snorkel masks. Diving with tanks is prohibited as the bubbles are thought to disturb the animals.

Whale sharks have spot patterns behind their gills which, like human fingerprints, are unique to each individual animal and so many are familiar from previous years. Though remarkably, more than half of those identified in St Helena's waters last year had never been recorded there or anywhere else, again raising the question of just where they had appeared from. Snorkelling close by the island to see the whale sharks can produce other surprises: one of the trust's staff found himself joined by Chilean devil rays and pods of bottlenose dolphins. I have been at sea off Jamestown when the sea was alive with around 400 dolphins leaping joyfully, following boats and fooling around, a fantastic sight.

In all, nearly 780 marine species have been recorded in St Helena, of which as many as 50 are endemic, such as the gloriously named St Helena butterflyfish and the marmalade razorfish. Its waters are extraordinary, remote, relatively pristine – apart from the depletion of a few coastal species – and yet the catastrophic impact that one introduced species, the goat, had on land is a constant reminder of the fragility of the remote island's marine ecosystem.

St Helena's waters were an obvious candidate for protection. But, unlike Ascension, our coalition played almost no role in campaigning for the protected area – declared by UK Foreign Office minister Sir Alan Duncan in September 2016, more than a year after the Conservative manifesto pledge to create a Blue Belt around the Overseas Territories. That was the Conservative government finally acting on its own 'big idea' without further prompting. Sir Alan also announced in that speech, given in Washington DC, that a law designating a marine protected area around the Pitcairn Islands in the Pacific had been brought into force and also that that Tristan da Cunha in the Atlantic, also governed from St Helena, was aiming to establish a marine protected area of its own – though details had yet to be worked out. The total area of ocean coming under meaningful protection in the Overseas Territories therefore added up to around 1.5 million square miles. That year, President Obama had trumped Chagos, until then the largest fully protected marine area in the world, by extending the Marine National Monument at Papahānaumokuākea in the Hawaiian island chain in the North Pacific to a total of 580,000 square miles. What Sir Alan politely did not say, perhaps because he was on US soil, was that the British Overseas Territories now represented the largest collection of marine conservation areas on Earth.[7] This was how far the Blue Belt had come.

My first voyage to St Helena was in the February after Sir Alan's announcement. The long voyage on the Royal Mail Ship *St Helena*, sadly now decommissioned, was a welcome opportunity to meet many prominent people from the island and important visitors among the other passengers. Our little conservation coalition had agreed that someone should support St Helena – the RSPB paid for some of the St Helena National Trust's work on land but its efforts did not extend to the sea. So we set up the St Helena National Trust's marine conservation department, which studied the whale sharks and created public awareness about the new marine protected area on the island. The lion's share of its work, though, was chivvying the St Helena government to finally put in place the fisheries legislation and the management plan that would safeguard the wildness of this remote, fragile and extraordinary place. In that endeavour, our staunchest allies were members of St Helena's fishing industry.

Remarkably, as in Lyme Bay, the original impetus for protecting St Helena's waters from industrial fishing – the most obvious threat – came from within its own fishing community. For many years, the leader in calling for foreign vessels to be expelled from St Helena's waters was the late Trevor 'Otto' Thomas. Otto was born in Hout Bay, a fishing port on the Cape in South Africa, to a St Helenian father – a 'Saint' – and a South African mother. He arrived on the island in 1969 and spent a decade or so fishing for tuna on some of the seamounts in St Helena's waters using the traditional 'one by one', hand-lining and rod-and-reel techniques, which have virtually no bycatch and have remained much the same since the sixteenth century.

The tuna in St Helena's waters are not there all the time as they migrate in unpredictably from the Gulf of Guinea. There are, I believe, mostly resident yellowfin and skipjack close by the island but to get to the largest and most valuable shoals of tuna it is necessary to motor all the way to one of the seamounts, which rear up from the abyssal plain close to the edge of St Helena's territorial waters: the one that comes closest to the surface is Cardno, some 180 nautical miles to the north.

What Otto saw out there on the seamounts made him angry. At that time, the St Helena government sold fishing licences to Asian fleets fishing for tuna with 80-mile longlines. They produced a huge bycatch, including turtles and blue sharks, which were finned and thrown back into the water alive. A lot of vessels also fished illegally. As the skipper of the offshore fishing vessel, the *Westerdam*, owned by the island's fishing corporation, Otto managed to arrest one of these poachers at sea. He told the illegal vessel that his fishing boat was a patrol vessel and that if the poacher did not consent to come back with him to Jamestown harbour he would call up the Royal Navy, which fortuitously happened to have a ship moored there. The fishing boat was duly impounded and its captain charged. Otto had made his point. St Helena's waters were being invaded at the expense of its own fishermen.

Frustrated by how little help he was getting from the St Helena government or the UK government in throwing out the foreign fleets that were plundering – or as we might now call it, de-wilding – St Helena's waters, by 1990 Otto had become an activist. He robed himself in the St Helena flag and led a march of hundreds of Saints down Main Street – one of the most perfectly preserved Georgian streets in the world – in Jamestown, the island's capital, in protest at the decision by the government to go on selling licences to Japanese vessels. I have seen a video of his march which created a strong tide of local opinion. His family still have the petition that he handed in to the castle. The governor of the time did not choose to come out to meet him.

Otto was employed by the hugely subsidised St Helena Fisheries Corporation, an arms-length company of the St Helena's government. The corporation ran a fish processing factory which was enlarged into the present industrial-scale building by a Falklands-based company called Argos that had a close relationship with the UK government. When Argos pulled out, the island was left with an antiquated, inefficient, energy-consuming fisheries plant, its freezers filled with outdated CFCs that should have been phased out in the 1980s. For years, this plant was the tail that wagged the dog. The whole St Helena economy is based on subsidies of around £30 million a year from the British taxpayer; the motivation of Treasury civil servants was to make the plant pay its way. This made feeding the plant with fish more important than tailoring the plant to the island's modest resources of tuna. However, no one could ever catch enough high-value tuna to make the present oversized plant pay its way, for it consumed more energy than any other activity on the island.

Long before the present fish plant was built, Otto did some trials of long-lining and purse-seining equipment for the then UK Department of Overseas Development. Otto found that purse-seining produced more low-value skipjack tuna than the original fish factory could handle and there was no way of canning it or exporting it. He did not like long-lining either because it produced so much bycatch of sharks and turtles. His son Waylon, now chairman of the fishermen's association, said: 'Having had all that experience, my dad thought St Helena should stick to what we know and are good at. We should be learning from our mistakes.' After he was successful in his efforts to bring about an end to the licensing of foreign vessels, Otto did not want St Helena to set up its own long-lining fleet to out-compete fishermen using traditional methods.

Yet when the time came to replace the vessel he skippered, the *Westerdam*, the fisheries corporation sent Otto to South Africa to pick up a new and larger vessel, ominously called *The Extractor*. The board insisted that the vessel was brought back to St Helena with 25 miles of longline. 'My dad said, "I don't want this thing loaded because this is not the direction St Helena is going in." The board insisted. There was a major blow-up between the crew and the owners of the boat. It got heated. Family issues came into it, as they often do in St Helena," says Waylon. Nobody really understands quite what happened but something snapped in Otto's head. In July 2014 he took his own life.

Otto's memorial is the creation of a marine protected area nearly the size of France. Sense has prevailed. Otto has won. St Helena has been rewilded – to the extent that industrial fishing is now banned and illegal fishing boats can be tracked by satellite – which means a reprieve for all the sharks, tunas and other great marine predators that are being caught, legally and otherwise, outside and which swim through the huge protected area. In time, it will mean no-take zones could be established around the island itself and perhaps the seamounts, too, to protect some of the island's more vulnerable endemic species. It will mean inshore species will have to be surveyed and conservation plans drawn up and a more satisfactory solution devised for the chute of barely filtered sewage that falls down a slimy green cliff into Jamestown harbour. All these things are more likely to happen in time because of the protected area.

In August 2021, a new law was finally passed requiring all fishing for tuna in the island's waters to be done by 'one-by-one' methods (the definition means one fisherman battles with one fish on hand-line or rod and line). The loss-making fisheries factory was offloaded onto a South African company – with a £500,000 dowry. This was controversial as it could just as well have been handed over to a collective of the island's own fishermen. The other concerning thing is that the St Helena government has set the quota for bigeye tuna at 600 tonnes, several times more than the island's fleet had ever caught. Bigeye is listed 'vulnerable' on the IUCN Red List so this was controversial too. Thankfully and sensibly, the new company has since mothballed the plant until it is made more efficient. And it has undertaken to work with the local fishermen using pole-and-line methods. The only thing yet to be seen is the split in the catch between the South African incomers and the local fleet. It would be a shame if local fishermen were to end up being disadvantaged in favour of foreign fishermen all over again.

There is a reason why I don't think that is going to happen. Shortly after the historic fisheries ordinance was published in August 2021, making Sir Alan Duncan's 'sustainable use marine protected area' a legal reality, Julie Thomas, Waylon's wife, a businesswoman who had lobbied for that legislation for five years, stood for election as a St Helena councillor and was duly elected, with the largest number of votes polled. The following week, she was elected chief minister. For a while at least, St Helena and its huge, remote part of the Atlantic, with its whale sharks and other intensely vulnerable marine wildlife, are in good hands.

I f St Helena is a lost world, I am told Tristan da Cunha feels like the end of the earth. It may be under the same governor as Ascension and St Helena but is even more remote – it is 1,700 miles from South Africa and 2,300 miles from the nearest shores of South America. The Queen's representatives have rarely been able to visit their subjects because of the wild and stormy seas which surround the active volcano that forms the only inhabited island, known to the locals as Tristan or 'the Settlement', and officially as Edinburgh of the Seven Seas. Islanders' boats have to be winched out of the ocean overnight because the sides of the island drop off into water a nautical mile deep, unlike Ascension or St Helena which have small continental shelves. The harbour is usable only 60 or so days a year because of heavy seas. Yet this small community of 244 people, on incomes of on average £5,000 a year, took a decision that would put most places on Earth to shame. They decided to turn 90 per cent of the waters around their group of islands into a marine protection zone (a fully protected or no-take area) extending to 270,000 square miles with no form of fishing or extraction between 50 and 200 miles from each island in the group.

For now, it means making some sacrifices, as the chief islander, James Glass, a descendant of one of the first British settlers, told *The Times*. It means fewer fishing vessels dropping in to trade basic supplies, such as tea bags, for the local rock lobsters, which are the island's principal export. Currently, tea bags are scarce. Eventually, the islanders hope, more cruise ships and scientists will sail the six days it takes to get here from Cape Town to see the extraordinary wildlife and more trade will resume.

I have not been to Tristan myself, though I have visited the wilds of west London with my colleagues Adrian Gahan and Chris Gorell Barnes to raise £1 million of the £4 million endowment fund lined up by major conservation donors that made the Tristanians' decision to protect their waters possible. So I am indebted to Jonathan Hall for his recollections of a journey he made there in January and February 2017. The expedition was organised by the US National Geographic Society's non-profit organisation, Pristine Seas, in conjunction with the Tristan government. The expedition was led by our friend Paul Rose, a veteran diver and expedition leader who I met in Ascension. As Hall remembers it: 'We were unbelievably lucky with the weather. We were able to land on all four islands of the Tristan group and see more of them than many Tristanians themselves have seen.

'The expedition brought the film of our voyage back to the Settlement where the whole close-knit community lives. Some 80 per cent of the population was there to watch the footage on a big screen. It was a great moment of pride and new understanding of what was out there for the islanders, most of whom had never visited the other islands in their own archipelago.

'The uninhabited islands, Nightingale, Inaccessible and Gough, are primeval, a nature lover's dream. It is as if humans have never been there. On Nightingale island, the sky actually darkens with millions of birds. The whole slope behind you is covered with birds and shearwaters scurry across your feet to get into their burrows. The rocks are covered with lines that millions of seabirds have used for centuries to climb up to jump off and fly out to sea. There are vast penguin colonies and seal colonies. You look at the beach and it looks like all the rocks are moving in front of you – but it is seals. Inshore, there are golden kelp forests which have only seven fish species: they are just there in massive numbers. The lobsters just sit there on rocks instead of hiding away in burrows: it is as if they have never been fished for. The scale of nature is hard to believe. You see a slope covered in white fluffy things that look like sheep. Then you realise that they are fat giant albatross chicks on their pedestal nests waiting to be fed by their parents. It was the most incredible place I have ever been.

'In one valley, visually a bit like moorland, there were so many spectacled petrels nesting that the sweet smell of seabirds was overpowering. Dawn and dusk are the most amazing times. You would think that the Tristan volcano – 2,060 metres high, last active in 2004 and often snow-capped – was smoking but it is seabirds, albatrosses pouring off the cliffs. Even with the rats and mice that have arrived on the main island since settlement in 1816, the bird life is still amazing. You can just imagine from the other islands what it was like before man came.' The RSPB is paying for the eradication of introduced mice that kill albatross chicks and even adult birds on Gough Island, a World Heritage Site and the furthest south. Tristan itself will be next if the community approves.

In terms of marine life, the expedition discovered many things, one of them that the islands, which are at the confluence of two ocean currents, one cold, one warm, are a refuge for migratory blue sharks, the most heavily fished sharks in the world and prized for their fins. At the time of Jonathan's trip, blue sharks were present in large numbers, along with seven-gill sharks, shortfin mako sharks, fin whales, humpback whales, sperm whales, dolphins and elephant seals – as well as 200,000 rockhopper penguins, 5 million shearwaters and 300,000 sub-Antarctic fur seals.

Hall remembers the Settlement as an extraordinarily welcoming and beautiful place, with the islanders tending their potato patches – which provide an essential component of their diet along with shellfish and fish – between the steep green cliffs of the volcano and the wide blue sea. The community, descended from some of the 1816 garrison that stayed behind, some American whalers and Italian sailors and several women from St Helena – the St Helena link is genetic as well as geographical – got together and made their decision as to how much ocean they were prepared to protect fully. They surprised the explorers by the extent of their ambition to conserve their unique environment. They opted to protect the largest area possible and to end bottom-trawling on seamounts, for they had seen the damage this had caused in drop-down camera footage. They also opted to ban a longline fishery for southern bluefin tuna once leased to Japan, just as, a few years earlier, they had chosen to get the rock lobster fishery, which provides the island's inhabitants with 80 per cent of their income, certified as sustainable by the Marine Stewardship Council without any prompting from outside NGOs. The islanders took a fiercely proud and forceful decision, in their own resourceful and impressively conservation-minded way.

Why did they do it? James Glass, the chief islander, told *The Times*: 'The Tristan community, although small, has always been deeply committed to conservation and understand only too well that the sea is our vital resource, for our economy and thus the livelihood and wellbeing of the islanders. We're proud that we can play a key role in preserving the health of the oceans. I hope others will be inspired to follow our example.' Glass accepts that the endowment fund, which will produce an income of about £120,000 a year, roughly the same as their government made from selling fishing licences, will not – for now – make up for the loss of traffic and trade with the island, which has left them short of such essentials as tea bags, but he said that making do with what was available was an aspect of Tristanian culture. They are actively looking at becoming more self-sufficient in energy and are dabbling in hydroponics – growing plants without soil.

Jonathan Hall believes the islanders chose the highest level of protection because the largest marine protected area in the Atlantic gives them a separate strand of income – through Blue Belt funding and 'science tourism' – for the future alongside the export of rock lobsters, which are shipped away by a fully commercial South African company that provides their only transport lifeline in and out of the island. The marine protection zone gives them more control over their environment, with satellite enforcement and, if necessary, patrol vessels to deal with the illegal fishing vessels, the lights of which the island's residents used to see at night. The Blue Belt should give the Tristanians more resources to manage their marine environment – and will, one day, mean more vessels bringing tea bags. Tristan will also have a trust fund that will provide at least some of the things their neglected island needs. Above all, Tristan's marine protection zone evidently gives the community a source of intense pride that they have safeguarded one of the richest places for wildlife on Earth.

The immensely difficult decisions that some of the inhabitants of the UK Overseas Territories have taken to protect their vast marine realms are humbling and stand as an example to the rest of the world, which seems to find it so difficult to banish damaging activities from all but the tiniest proportion of its seas. Each of these territories, at least those of them that so far have chosen to be full members of the Blue Belt, provides a different example of how remote communities can profitably co-exist with, and benefit from, wild nature, rather than over-exploiting it. They contrast sharply with the waters elsewhere in the oceans. One can imagine these islands' immense natural riches being a chosen destination of the expedition cruises of the future, though these will, of course, need to be properly managed, on the lines of those to Antarctica today. Let's hope that the incentive has now been created for people to develop ingenious ways of showcasing their riches, to visitors or virtually. For coming generations, wilderness is likely to be an even more valuable experience and people will surely be prepared to travel a long way, even by sea, to enjoy it.

Ultimately for me, though, the inspiring example set by these leading UK Overseas Territories must inevitably be compared with the pitiful ambition shown so far in conserving marine resources in our once-fertile and heavily altered waters back home.

6

Dinosaurs of the Dogger

'*The reasonable man adapts himself to the world; the unreasonable one persists in adapting the world to himself. Therefore all progress depends on the unreasonable man.*'

George Bernard Shaw, *Man and Superman*, 1903

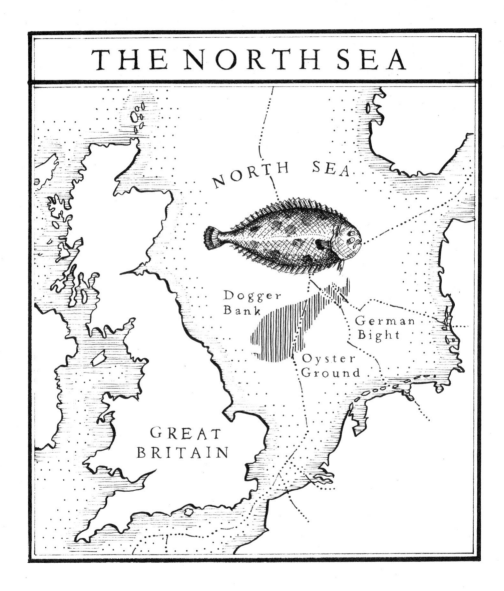

THE NORTH SEA

NORTH SEA

Dogger
Bank

German
Bight

Oyster
Ground

GREAT
BRITAIN

A large granite boulder rests on Dogger Bank, in the heart of the North Sea. It has my name painted on it. This three-tonne lump of rock remains there as a permanent deterrent to any vessel coming to trawl or dredge. My name is on it because for the first time in 40 years of writing about environmental matters, over half of it as a correspondent for a conservative newspaper, I crossed the line. I played a part in a direct action because I believed the time had come to make a point. Something absurd and wrong was going on. Europe's offshore marine 'protected' areas were officially described as such but, scandalously, they were completely unprotected from even the most damaging fishing methods. Dogger Bank was called a marine protected area, all 4,600 square miles of it on the British side, yet there was about as much chance of marine life surviving there as a hedgehog on a motorway. This had been going on for a decade and more, since offshore reserves were designated in European waters, because of a long-unresolved legal conflict between European environmental and fisheries law. If we were going to rewild the sea and allow nature to restore our muddy and altered waters this was the place to make our watery stand.

Dogger Bank is the Atlantis of the North Sea, the flooded remnant of a land bridge to Continental Europe which foundered 8,000 years ago as the waters rose after the last Ice Age. It is mostly sandbank, 20 to 60 metres down, with some drowned peat bogs or 'moorlog' around the edges of it which show up on O.T. Olsen's

1883 atlas. Currents and tides wash over the bank and four large wind farms are being built on it. Nutrients swirl up from deeper water which feed plankton, which in turn attract other marine organisms. Harbour porpoises, minke whales and large flocks of seabirds forage there, feeding on sand eels, a small species of fish that hibernates in burrows during the winter or when threatened. Cod, plaice and sole are still caught on the bank – the name 'Dogger' probably derives from the two-masted Dutch boats that used to trawl for cod there in medieval times. Dogger once even had its own piscatorial megafauna. Giant halibut the size of a man were caught, along with common skate as big as a dinner table. These fish are gone, along with other probable denizens of the bank, such as angel sharks. Scientists studying rare sharks in the North Sea found that there were fewer sharks in marine protected areas than in surrounding areas of the sea.[1] Why? Because the supposedly protected areas – the 'paper parks' – were where most of the commercially targeted fish species were, so they were the more heavily fished.

Since the 1890s, when steam-powered trawling began, there has been what the writer and restaurateur Henry Dimbleby, in his 'National Food Strategy',[2] has called 'a staggering decline in overall fish abundance' in UK waters. Cod landings have declined by 87 per cent, hake by 95 per cent, halibut by a staggering 99.8 per cent. In the 1830s, small sailing vessels on Dogger Bank could catch a tonne of halibut a day. Today, all fishing across the area – in UK, Dutch, German and Danish sectors – lands less than two tonnes of halibut a year. Whether seen simply as the squandering of Europe's food resources, or as the relentless destruction of a wild ecosystem, or as the stirrer-up of carbon from marine sediments that find their way into the atmosphere, no form of fishing did more harm than bottom trawling, said Dimbleby. It was the first time a government publication had made the case so strongly. It was a sign that the tide of opinion was changing – and perhaps an indication of government decisions to come.

By the time Dimbleby published his damning statement about trawling, we – BLUE and the French charity BLOOM – had already made a successful legal complaint against the European Union for allowing electric pulse trawls (highly experimental trawls that use electric currents to zap fish into the net instead of the usual beams and ticker chains) in protected areas such as Dogger Bank. The European Commission had given a 'derogation' – a legal exemption – for this otherwise banned electric fishing technique, without any reference to where it could be used. This meant the fishing fleets could use it everywhere in the southern North Sea, including all offshore protected areas. Dutch universities and fishermen argued that electric trawls were environmentally friendly. They said boats towing pulse trawls used less fuel because the pulse equipment was not as heavy as a beam trawl. Yet no one had properly examined the impact on the seabed or the creatures that lived there.

A study by the UK's Centre for Environment, Fisheries and Aquaculture Science (CEFAS) subsequently found that less than half the number of seabed species were present in the areas fished with electric trawls. There were also 2.6 times fewer soles and thornback rays. This confirmed what inshore fishermen had been saying: pulse trawling was destroying their fishing grounds and 'leaving behind an aquatic graveyard'.

How did the European Union get itself into this stupid position? The EU has a biodiversity strategy: 'a comprehensive, ambitious and long-term plan to protect nature and reverse the degradation of ecosystems'. In the sea, however, this has no basis in reality, for the laws the strategy is based on are not applied. In the European Union, unlike in the United States, citizens are not, as yet, permitted to sue the government for breaking its own laws. So the EU's strategy is pure hogwash.

With Brexit, the law would change on the UK side of the sea. Citizens would be able to sue the government for not applying its own laws, as they can in Common Law countries, such as the UK, the US and Australia. This offered the biggest opportunity in decades to heal the North Sea and probably EU waters too because of the precedent it would set.

Back in the early spring of 2020, Tom Appleby, BLUE's legal adviser, and I met up with Will McCallum, Greenpeace's ocean campaigner, and agreed that we would launch the legal case for the proper protection of Dogger Bank while Greenpeace would dramatise the need to stop bottom trawling. It was better if we did not ask how.

Greenpeace had been shadowing fishing activity on Dogger Bank all summer. Now, on Monday 21 September, the Greenpeace vessel *Esperanza* began dumping a series of three-tonne boulders on the bank to protect it from bottom trawling and dredging. Chris Thorne from Greenpeace told *The Times*: 'Allowing bottom trawling in a protected area established to protect the seabed is equivalent to allowing bulldozers to plough through a protected forest.'

A furious Barrie Deas, chief executive of the National Federation of Fishermen's Organisations – which represents many Dutch-owned companies that trawl on Dogger for sole – accused Greenpeace of endangering trawlermen's lives. The boulders, he said, could catch a boat's nets and cause it to capsize. We thought this was nonsense, as Greenpeace had marked the boulders on the electronic charts which fishermen use to avoid the many wrecks on Dogger. Deas called, without any sense of irony, for a police investigation on this legal technicality – even though by law the vessels should not have been there in the first place. He appeared to have zero public support. This was looking like one of Greenpeace's most inspired pieces of protest theatre.

Greenpeace also revealed what the fishing vessels they had been following had been doing. Not only were these vessels bottom-trawling in a protected area but 11 trawlers were fishing with their automatic identification systems (AIS) switched off, presumably so as not to give away where they were fishing to their competitors. AIS is an international legal requirement for boats above a certain tonnage because it averts the danger of collision in poor weather or at night. It is also a legal requirement under the Common Fisheries Policy. If people were worried about endangering life, what about this?

After dropping 17 granite boulders, the *Esperanza* headed back to Hamburg to load up some more. At which point, Greenpeace found itself offered an unexpected meeting with Rebecca Pow, a junior environment minister in the UK government. She ticked them off for dropping boulders in the sea illegally. She promised that the government would use the opportunity offered by Brexit to improve the management of offshore marine protected areas – but evidently this was not to be any time soon.

Two days later, I heard from Will McCallum that the *Esperanza* had spotted a window in the September gales and was steaming out to drop another load of boulders on Dogger, this time with celebrities' names painted on them. The *Esperanza* steamed at full speed towards Dogger and a Royal Navy helicopter was scrambled to ask it to desist. Greenpeace needed support. I came to a decision. As a charity executive, I could not officially support the Greenpeace action without a lengthy board discussion but as a fellow campaigner, I could give a signal that we were on the same side and that our coalition would not be split by the technical offence of dropping an object on the seabed. The answer was to do it in a personal capacity. I gave it a few moments more thought, called my chairman, Arlo Brady, and told him my plan, which he approved. I WhatsApped Will, who was co-ordinating the operation from London, and asked if my name could be painted on one of the boulders to be dropped. There was a short pause. Then he texted back, 'Your name is being 'scribed now.'

It wasn't quite storming the barricades but it was, I believe, a decisive moment in our campaign. Greenpeace's action and our legal case, taken together, may yet turn out to be the critical moment in rewilding the UK's seas.

There are still fishermen who say I was endangering their colleagues' lives. Yet I knew when I supported Greenpeace that there were inshore fishermen in East Anglia who had fought alongside us against pulse trawling, cheering us on. They would have been delighted to see the beam trawlers forced out of Dogger Bank and other supposedly protected areas because they knew it would have saved fish, which might one day have been caught in much smaller nets over a longer period of time and therefore had more time to breed. One of them even offered a rude slogan he would like painted on a boulder if Greenpeace intended to drop any more.

I believe in the law. I believe in the rights of property. I accept that properly consultative, legislative change is slow and the result is a compromise between various interests. Yet in this case, due process had become a decade of prevarication. Something had to be done and it was a once-in-four-decades opportunity to do it. Nature has its needs too, some of which are urgent as the ecosystem is deteriorating and most of the official indicators about the health of the sea are flashing orange or red.[3]

The seas present a unique legislative problem. They are our commons, owned by everyone and no one, but within 200 miles of the shore they are technically owned by the citizens of individual coastal states. It is right that the public interest should prevail, not those of shadowy 'stakeholders', many of whom turn out to be fishing or fish-farming companies with foreign owners (around half of the quota owned by members of England's National Federation of Fishermen's Organisations is thought to be owned by Dutch companies and most of the Scottish salmon-farming industry is foreign-owned).

The public interest is different from the industrial fishing or farming interest, though people once used to think it was the same because trawlers brought in abundant quantities of cheap food. Equally, people often assume the farming of carnivorous fish is reducing the consumption of wild fish, when actually it is not (see chapter eight). Now some commercial fish stocks around the UK coast have collapsed or been reduced to a tiny remnant of what they were. Most cod consumed in UK is imported from Iceland or the Barents Sea. People rightly perceive that the industrial vessels have been responsible for wiping out stocks of fish such as cod and damaging fish habitat, largely because the big fishing organisations lobby hard to catch more than they should. The public reaction to the Greenpeace boulder-drop generated unanimous support. This surprised us. Skimming through the comments below *The Times*'s stories about the action on Dogger, it was hard to find any that were critical. Indeed, Greenpeace seemed to have had the best press since its anti-whaling campaigns of the 1970s.

Our threat to sue the government for not complying with its own laws had begun to pay off. We met fisheries minister Victoria Prentis, who told us that the Marine Management Organisation was shortly to announce a call for evidence about Dogger Bank and four other sites. Pressure seemed to be working.

When this invitation arrived, we duly started listing the evidence that Dogger was the key to restoring the whole damaged North Sea ecosystem. We were fairly sure that after a century and a half of being battered by increasingly efficient bottom trawls and recently by pulse and scallop gears that there were few endangered species left on Dogger. Then we discovered, to our amazement, that at least one might still be there.

For quite separate reasons, we had been looking at the potential of British rivers for reintroducing sturgeon. Sturgeon are living dinosaurs, thought to have evolved as long as 200 million years ago. They grow to nearly 20 feet long if you let them and are the property of the Crown if caught within three miles of the shore. They are now listed as critically endangered on the IUCN Red List of

Endangered Species but long ago they were a relatively common sight in British rivers. Fish traps, over-exploitation, river netting and building of weirs and dams put paid to that. Yet sturgeon still turn up very occasionally. They are thought to have strayed from the naturally spawning population in the Gironde in France or, more recently, from reintroduction programmes in the continental rivers Oder and Elbe. Unlike salmon, the majority of which will return to their native rivers, sturgeon seem inclined to explore other river systems.

Rory Moore, BLUE's international projects manager, had been investigating where sturgeon were caught in the past as a prelude for a possible reintroduction into British rivers. The UK Sturgeon Alliance, of which he was part, was compiling evidence that sturgeon had once been, or perhaps still were, a species native to the UK. This research, overseen by Steve Colclough, formerly of the Environment Agency, threw up one unexpected result.

Steve compiled 5,000 records of sturgeon captured in UK waters dating back to 1700. Specifically, there were nine records of large sturgeon being caught on Dogger Bank between 1852 and 1977. These appeared to show that it was once an important feeding ground for large adult sturgeon once they had left the estuaries and shallow coastal waters where they fed as juveniles. Steve found a picture dated 1925 of a huge sturgeon of 262kg caught in a trawl off Dogger on the wall of a Lowestoft pub. There was also a picture in existence of another large sturgeon caught by a British trawler off Dogger Bank in 1977. Bizarrely, it was put on display at Harrods department store.

Steve and his network believed that buried within the records

were many more historic cases of sturgeon caught on Dogger Bank
and in the German Bight than was currently thought. The skippers
of trawlers that went out deliberately to catch sturgeon did not
always declare where they caught the hundreds that they landed.
There are records of 2,254 sturgeon being captured between 1850
and 1987 in the central and southern North Sea, a big area. Some
1,700 of the records in the database are from 'directed fisheries' –
instances where fishermen went out deliberately to catch sturgeon.
It appears now that the records may show catches of two very similar species of fish, the European sturgeon and the Atlantic sturgeon,
though these are not identified separately.

Satellite tracking of juvenile sturgeon reintroduced to the German rivers and migrating to sea has found that juveniles stay in the
less-saline waters of the German Bight and in the estuaries of the
eastern North Sea. From these old catch records, it now appeared
that when sturgeon matured, they migrated out further to productive feeding grounds in the central North Sea, such as Dogger Bank.

If one was to treat the North Sea as a wildlife habitat instead as
a kind of prairie to be combined regularly with harvesting machines,
how would one ideally protect endangered fish such as the sturgeon? As with any migratory fish, if one wanted to ensure its
recovery one would have to protect its spawning habitat – in fresh
water – as well as its feeding grounds, out at sea. The Oslo and Paris
Convention (OSPAR), to which all north-east Atlantic nations are
signatories, recommends that the sturgeon is protected 'in all life
stages'. Though the sturgeon is named specifically in the European
Habitats Directive because of its rarity, and though it is clearly vulnerable to trawling, it seems quite clear that nobody has considered

protecting enough of its range to ensure its continued survival, which seems even more ridiculous given Germany's efforts to reintroduce them. You might even be forgiven for assuming that Europe's fisheries authorities regarded it as a pest.

It seemed incredible that these dinosaur fish could still be holding on in our heavily altered seas. If the needs of the sturgeon were fully considered and places were set aside where they might survive, how long would it take to see a revival of these extraordinary fish? Maybe a couple of decades? That would make the German Bight and Dogger Bank yet another kind of Jurassic Park. We said so in our submission to the government's call for evidence on Dogger Bank.

In the autumn of 2020, there came another timely reminder of just how fragile life is for the sea's biggest creatures off our industrially fished shores. Fishermen and divers in the Inner Sound by the Isle of Skye found more than 100 eggs of the flapper skate, a creature once known as the common skate, which was formerly recorded as being caught on Dogger Bank. More, however, were discovered to have been lost to dredging.

The name 'common skate' is a misnomer, not just because it is now vanishingly rare. The not-so-common skate, it was realised in 2009, is actually two species with overlapping ranges, the blue and the flapper skate. Both are listed as critically endangered, which means they are now in greater danger of extinction, in terms of risk, than the mountain gorilla or giant panda. The flapper skate, as it is now called, is huge. It can grow up to over 2.5 metres long. Its eggs, which are laid in great sacs known as mermaid's purses, take an

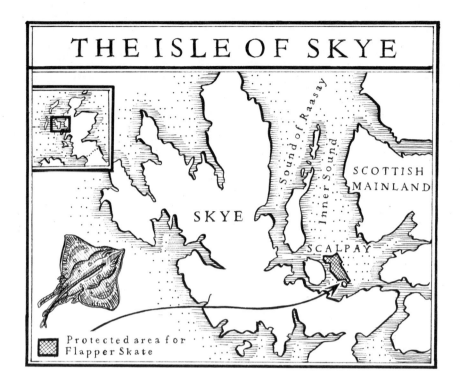

extraordinary 18 months to hatch, making them extremely vulnerable to disturbance. The flapper skate takes many years to mature and has few young so it takes an astonishing 14 years for its population to double in size, even if it gets the chance to do so. Left alone, these giants can live to be 100 years old. They are uniquely ill-equipped to survive in waters that are frequently trawled or dredged.

A year before, local fishermen and scientists had alerted Marine Scotland to the secret location of the flapper skate nesting site. But so far, Marine Scotland had done nothing. Our Morven Robertson found some funds, hired a boat and enabled some amateur divers to go and find out if the skates' eggs were still alive and in need of protection. The local divers found that one of the sites discovered the previous year had been totally destroyed by scallop dredgers. They went to the other secret site, nestled in rocks near the Isle of Skye, and luckily found 100 or more eggs alive – the largest such flapper skate nursery ever documented.

Thanks to these divers, and our frantic efforts, film of the nesting site soon began rolling on Sky TV news. Two weeks later, the flapper skate featured for eight minutes on BBC TV's *Autumnwatch*. The growing understanding that Scotland has its own marine mega-fauna, now vanishingly rare, lit a beacon for rewilding. A few months later, and just before a six months' close season for trawling and scallop dredging ended, the Scottish government announced a no-take zone to protect the flapper skate nests. This we welcomed even though it was only 2.3 square miles in size and fell short of a larger area recommended by NatureScot, the Scottish government's nature advisers, that would also have protected delicate and important features in the area, such as maerl beds and flame shell reefs. The no-take zone also – rather spitefully – excluded the creelers (the Scottish word for potters) who had flagged up the existence of the skate nursery in the first place and who would have done little harm to the skate with their creels, as well as recreational fishermen who were unlikely to have bothered the skate either.

The Scottish political context may explain this bizarrely unchari-table behaviour by Marine Scotland. An alliance of fishermen and conservationists was trying to push trawlers and dredgers out beyond three miles and restore an inshore limit for trawling to pro-tect nursery areas such as this. The Scottish government was opposed. This appeared to be a way for the government led by the Scottish National Party to give in to popular pressure to save endangered wildlife while not giving an inch on its dogged determination to defend trawling.

I believe the skids are now under the practice of trawling in protected areas. There is hope that what I called for in my book, *The End of the Line* – the protection of 30 per cent of UK waters in a meaningful way – might be achieved in my lifetime. What happens in these protected areas should be monitored, for it could be an example to the world, not just for the biodiversity it brings back and its contribution to the health of marine life but also for the carbon-absorbing forests of animals and plants on the seabed that it allows to flourish. Nature may need a little help – perhaps by reintroducing species such as the flapper skate to Dogger Bank.

Enthusiasts for banning trawling should understand that other fishing methods are not without their problems, either. For example, static gill nets can kill whales, dolphins and porpoises – as well as large fish such as skates and sturgeon – and can overfish as much as any other method. There is evidence, however, that it is both ecologically and economically advantageous to prioritise artisanal methods within 3, 6, 12, even 40 miles of the coast. It is also becoming clearer that both ecologically and economically it is advantageous to set aside large areas which are not fished at all.

The discovery of the common skate nursery is a reminder of just how inadequately small the areas currently set aside to protect endangered marine animals actually are. Wilding on land has meant putting back large animals that once shaped the landscape. There is comparatively little scientific evidence of what trophic cascades (see chapter one) large predators might bring about in healing the sea – though I have already offered the example of bluefin driving up baitfish to be accessible to seabirds as one case in point. Our nearby seas are just too altered to understand the niche that some large marine animals filled but common sense tells you that it must bring about stupendous changes. Maybe that is something we will see in the future as marine protected areas such as Dogger and around Skye mature and nature takes a lead. What would be the impact on the marine ecosystem of bringing back the flapper skate, the giant halibut, multiple shark species and the sturgeon, along with the habitat they used to live in? We simply do not know. Thanks to the promised protection of Dogger Bank, I am excited to say, one day we will.

There is another lesson we are only just beginning to learn. We have always assumed that de-wilding the sea was necessary and inevitable so that we had enough fish to eat. It turns out, from the example of places like Lyme Bay where trawling has stopped, that it would actually have been more productive, economically and eco-logically, to leave the sea wilder than it is today, which would grow more fish. It is entirely possible to harvest those fish by other, more selective means. There are no very good reasons to go on trawling. It is beginning to look as though the industrial trawl fleets which have reduced four out of five cod populations round the British Isles to a state of collapse are, metaphorically speaking, the real dinosaurs.

7

Paradise Lost?

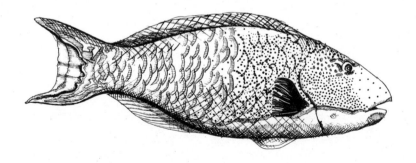

'Renowned for its prestigious five-star luxury resorts set on their own private islands, the Maldives offers world-class facilities with everything from gourmet dining in underwater restaurants to personalised treatments in overwater spas. Accommodation is luxurious and spacious, with beach villas ideal for family holidays, and overwater bungalows perfect for a romantic Maldives honeymoon.'

luxtripper.co.uk, 2021

THE MALDIVES

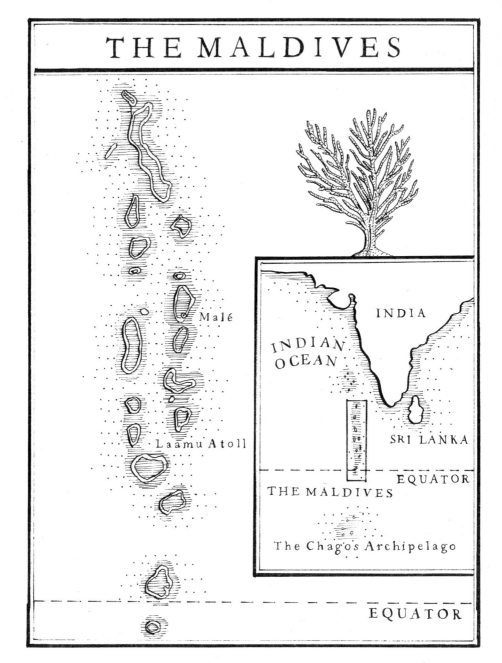

Malé

Laamu Atoll

INDIAN
OCEAN

INDIA

SRI LANKA

EQUATOR

THE MALDIVES

The Chagos Archipelago

EQUATOR

There are few more awe-inspiring sights from the air than the coral atolls of the Indian Ocean. These rings of white coral sand bordered by green mangroves and seagrass, set in seas of improbably deep blue, have been called the last paradise on Earth. They are duly marketed as such by a tourist industry that is growing at a ferocious pace, now focusing its marketing activities in China as it did before in the West. There are some places in the world, such as the fast-warming Arctic, where time appears to be passing faster than in others. The Maldives is another such place. This country of 26 coral atolls is economically dependent upon its appeal as a tourist destination. As I write, 135 new resorts are proposed – roughly a doubling of the present number – plus several new airports. They all involve building out onto the underwater coral with reinforced concrete.

Some of these artificial islands are visible from the air as the plane begins its descent into Velana International Airport, next to the country's capital on the small, crowded island of Malé, where few tourists go. Yet a waterfront restaurant in Malé, a low-lying island whose beaches have almost all been destroyed by artificial wharfs and rock armour, is an excellent place to contemplate the likely fate of the world's coral islands. Rewilding could play a vital role in defending these coral platforms, and the lives of the people who live on them, as sea levels rise.

There is a lot of the natural world still to enjoy in the Maldives. The light is startlingly sharp. The sunsets are jaw-dropping. The warm-bath temperatures are welcoming to snorkellers and divers who have the chance of seeing manta rays, turtles and whale sharks. Thanks to early conservation efforts, primarily due to pressure from the tourist industry, the bigger animals – sharks, rays, turtles, whales and dolphins, and the spectacular Napoleon wrasse – have been protected and their numbers maintained. With every successive visit, however, regular visitors observe a lessening in the number and variety of colourful reef fish, for reasons that will become evident. And here the climate crisis feels very close as the whole country is on average only a metre above sea level. The former president, Mohamed Nasheed, now the speaker of Parliament, once held a cabinet meeting under water to underline the danger of his country disappearing beneath the rising seas if global emissions of carbon dioxide were not curbed soon.

Out there in the atolls, snorkelling over the shallow reefs with their sinister patches of bleached and dead coral, it is clear change is under way. In the 1998 climatic warming event, replicated again in 2016, more than 90 per cent of all corals bleached and died – only growing back to some extent. When I was in Laamu atoll three years ago, there were worrying amounts of dead coral around. I hear this is growing back rapidly in some places but not others. The gloomy prevailing scientific view is that by 2050, the warming events will come so often that the corals will not get the chance to recover between them.

There are optimists and pessimists about the coral reefs, with the pessimists now in the majority. I am an optimist but I will concede the situation is precarious. There were corals around millions of years ago when the seas were hotter and more acidic than they are today, so I believe that evolution will eventually see some of the corals come through, though clearly some will be lost. I side with Michael Webster, a research scientist at New York University, who is unusually confident about that. He told the *Guardian* in the context of Australia's Great Barrier Reef: 'For evolution to occur quickly usually requires a lot of death: that is the natural selection signal. Right now, we're in the ugly beginning of that process. I believe a lot of corals are going to get through this bottleneck, they're not going to go extinct, they're going to figure out a way to keep pace with climate change, so long as we give them some room.'

That's the challenge.

In this scenario – which is the only one we can contemplate without despair – we have not only got to deal globally with the carbon dioxide emissions as fast as we know how, we also need to act locally, on poor reef management and overfishing – precisely so that we give the corals that room. Pollution – locally in places from leaking sewage pipes and land drains – and more generally overfishing are dangers as insidious as climate change. We cannot just ignore these factors – as too many coral nations do.

In the Maldives, there is a tussle going on with these bad boys, which can only get bigger as the tourist developments increase. It is far from clear who the winner is going to be. The democratic government of the Maldives is finally getting some things right, but others not so fast. I remember speaking to a previous Maldivian environment minister who wanted urgent help in dealing with leaking, developing-world sewage pipes on the home islands, where most people live, which were killing reefs due to the excessive nutrients in the sewage. I did not know how to help but at least he was asking the right questions.

Getting control of overfishing and local pollution of the reefs may be crucial to coral islands' very existence. There is now fascinating new evidence to suggest that, instead of being doomed to destruction, the Maldives islands could actually adapt and grow higher as sea levels rise, provided its reefs stay healthy. These islands persisted when sea levels were 0.5–1 metre higher than they are today, 4,000–2,000 years ago.[1] They rose when the sea levels rose because of the sediment deposited by storms. For the natural processes to be able to shape and lift these islands once again, there needs to be sufficient sediment produced by their reefs. Currently, the bleaching damage to coral reefs may actually benefit atoll islands over the next decades, as plenty of dead coral will wash up in storms, provided coastal flooding can happen naturally, but over the long term, damage to the coral reef ecosystem will leave atoll islands without enough sediment to adapt naturally to sea-level rise.[2] This adaptation can only happen if reefs are able to function as they should. This means the corals have to be kept clean and healthy by plenty of reef-cleaning fish. They need to be wilder than they currently are.

Happily, some of the positive developments elsewhere in the world are slowly filtering though into practice in the Maldives, such as marine protected areas, one of which has recently been announced at Laamu Atoll, partly thanks to campaigning by the head of the local charity we have backed, Maldives Resilient Reefs, and its local partners. Its chairperson, Shaha Hashim, along with her colleague based in UK, Vivienne Evans, has being inspiring and persuading local fishermen to protect spawning aggregations of grouper – a reef fish. These astonishing nocturnal gatherings of increasingly rare species are vulnerable if their locations become known and reef fish are only now coming under management by the Maldives' rather old-fashioned Fisheries Ministry. We must hope grouper protection measures progress quickly as they are already too late for some spawning aggregations.

The big paradox of the Maldives is that it has a pole-and-line fishery for tuna that employs thousands of fishermen, which is socially fairer and less ecologically damaging than industrial fishing methods. But this industry depends on catching fish for bait. The catching of baitfish takes the largest quantity of reef fish but local people and tourists in resorts also eat them, and some are transported live to the Far East. Fishing for reef fish is largely unregulated and the principal reason why there are fewer reef fish for the tourists to see. My colleague Rory Moore found himself underneath one bait-fishing boat which suddenly dropped its net on the reef where he was diving in ten fathoms of water. He was able to get out of the way but it gave him a fright – and the rest of us a salutary lesson in what goes on unmonitored and out of sight.

Fish caught for bait are mostly plankton-eaters, important to the health of the reef. One of the most frequently caught is the beautiful yellowback fusilier, which left alone can form huge spectacular shoals which delight divers and snorkellers. The fate of the yellowback fusilier is an example of the frequently loss-making fishing industry inflicting damage on the profitable tourist industry, and potentially the future of the coral atolls themselves. It is perverse. The Maldives – and any other coral reef country – ignores the overfishing of reef fish at its peril as it may be decreasing its chances of growing higher as sea levels rise.

Successive Maldivian fisheries ministers have promised to breed milkfish as bait for the tuna fishery but, though much development aid has been spent to that end, there is little sign of this happening. For it is more expensive than simply netting the reefs. Milkfish is what politicians bring up when overseas consumers of Maldivian tuna raise the issue of baitfish. This is missing the point, which is that the Maldives, and other coral atoll countries, need to rewild their reefs for their very survival.

While it is easy to get the impression that time is speeding up and things are getting rapidly worse in the Maldives, ecologically speaking, some of the right things are happening more quickly thanks in part to the power of social media and the enthusiasm of the young. Shaha, Viv and a coalition of Maldivian colleagues successfully harnessed the power of civil society to educate the tourism industry about the need to protect seagrass – which is both a carbon sink and a wildlife habitat – and persuaded the tourism minister to scrap the traditional guidance to resorts to pull it up. The all-powerful tourism ministry had, until then, put out the tidy-minded view that seagrass should be pulled up because tourists expected to see white sand beaches devoid of leaf litter. The tourism minister sensibly listened to ecological (and carbon-saving) sense and withdrew this advice.

Viv and Sha were also part of a successful social media campaign to stop the killing of parrotfish, which clean the reefs of algae. Seasoned fishermen do not kill parrotfish if they can help it but during the Covid pandemic when many Maldivians working in the capital, Malé, and tourist resorts went back to their home islands, the parrotfish were getting a pasting from the uninitiated. Social media is a powerful thing in the Maldives, where the islands are far apart and almost everyone owns a smart phone. The ban on catching parrot-fish came in quickly and was communicated fast. I have faith that, were it left to the upcoming generation of Maldivians, the rapid erosion of their marine resources that is visibly going on around them would eventually be brought under control.

Inevitably, the Maldives's success in looking after its reefs will end up being compared with the deserted, unfished but equally climate-challenged atolls of the Chagos Archipelago marine reserve, over 600 miles to the south. As I mentioned in chapter two, when it was designated in 2010, Chagos was the largest no-take marine pro-tected area in the world with around 50 per cent of the remaining healthy corals in the Indian Ocean. It will be interesting to see if, as sea temperatures rise, the islands retain any more of their corals than elsewhere. Much has happened to the health of the reefs in the decade or so since the reserve was declared as a result of some strong El Niño warming events.[3] Sea turtle numbers are up, as are fish – almost certainly the result of the ban on fishing. There have been changes, too, to the disputed legal situation over the Cha-gos. World sympathy and the balance of the law have been shifting towards the Mauritian claim to the islands.

After the creation of the Chagos marine reserve in 2010, which it opposed on the grounds that its historic rights to fish were being taken away, Mauritius initiated legal proceedings against Brit-ain and the Maldives – which had made claims to extend its continental shelf further south, affecting the outer boundary of Chagos waters. As a result, the International Court of Justice and the UN General Assembly issued a legal opinion in 2019 saying that the decolonisation of Mauritius from the UK (that is, including the Chagos) had not been lawfully completed and that the UK should end its administration of the Chagos archipelago as rapidly as possible. This the UK has effectively ignored, saying the legal opinion was only advisory.[4] The official UN map, however, now shows Chagos as part of Mauritius, the UN Food and Agriculture Organisation no longer recognises the UK to be the coastal state and the Universal Postal Union has decided that the British Indian Ocean Territory belongs to Mauritius so its postage stamps are no longer valid. Scientists working in BIOT have been told they need Mauritian work permits.

The British grip on the territory weakened further in February 2022 when Mauritius paid for a cruise ship to take a delegation led by Mauritius-based Chagossians to land and raise the Mauritian flag on some of the depopulated islands. The sympathy of the world was gripped by pictures of Rosamonde Bertin,[5] standing in the ruins of a church and the hospital where she gave birth to her first child before everyone on Salomon atoll was forcibly deported by the British to Mauritius and the Seychelles. One would need a heart of stone not to sympathise with the exiled Chagossians and want the wrong done to them to be rectified, which the British government has been slow in doing. Yet, it should not be assumed that the interests of the Chagossians are synonymous with those of the Mauritian political elite, which could be accused of using the language of human rights to advance its own agenda. The marginalising of Chagossians within Mauritius is routinely pointed out by UK-based Chagossians. Frankie Bontemps, a second-generation Chagossian who now lives in the UK, described the highly publicised landing on the islands by Mauritius-based Chago-ssians and officials to the *Sunday Times* as a 'political stunt by the Mauritians'.[6] Another UK-based Chagossian Mylene Augustin told the *Sunday Mirror*: 'Both Mauritius and Britain are still treating us like we're slaves. When they deported us, the British said they needed the islands to protect the world. Who's protecting us?'[7] That remains a very pertinent question.

Right now, the UK shows no immediate sign of giving up possession of the islands which it has held since 1814. But if, as now seems inevitable, the British government is shamed into giving up the Chagos one day, serious questions about both human rights and the marine environment will have to be asked of Mauritius's leaders. First is how they are planning to act in the best interests of the many groups of Chagossians, whose diaspora ranges as far as the Seychelles and the UK as well as Mauritius? To whom would land rights be granted – Chagossians or just Mauritian citizens? And what are Mauritius's intentions towards the marine protected area declared in 2010 – which it opposed?

Mauritius is a demonstrably poor steward of its own waters. Henry Smith, the Conservative MP for Crawley, where the largest Chagossian population in the UK lives, described the Mauritian government's record on conservation as 'abysmal'. He said: 'Last year, there was a tanker spillage of over 1,000 tonnes off Mauritius and the government was very slow to act.' Mauritius currently has 0.009 per cent of its waters in marine protected areas.[8] Mauritius is also the home not only of Princes Tuna, part of the Japanese-owned multinational Mitsubishi Corporation which owns a huge canning operation there, but also of a foreign-owned purse-seine fleet (see the next chapter). These would presumably be given little – or no – incentive to adapt their fishing methods to promote biodiversity and rewilding. If Mauritius wants to take over Chagos, it needs to be very clear about its intentions or the Chagossians are likely to end up no better off than before, with their rich waters being fished industrially all around them.

Advocates of a settlement between Britain and Mauritius say that the future of the British-government-designated Chagos marine protected area should be included in the talks[9] and that guarantees for perpetuating the Chagos reserve to some extent could be written into an agreement. While it is hard to see how these guarantees could be enforced, it is emphatically worth trying because it is clear that commercial fishing by industrial fleets would not benefit the Chagossians, since any licence revenue would go to the Mauritian government who would likely not invest it in Chagos or fisheries enforcement. Artisanal and subsistence fishing to serve the inhabited islands would be a different matter. It would be far better to develop high-end tourism (which needs to be carefully managed for all the reasons clearly on show in the Maldives) based on the very special pristine environment of the Chagos reefs and waters. The islanders, if they chose to return, would stand to gain from local employment and money spent by tourists on reef-based experiences.

Ultimately, whoever holds sovereignty over them, the waters of the Chagos remain of great value to scientists and the rest of the world as one of the most pristine, unpolluted and fully functioning tropical marine ecosystems on Earth. Scientists will go on wanting to monitor how well they recover from heat-induced bleaching. Others will want to chart the recovery of highly migratory fish populations as a result of the reserve and the potential of a reserve to safeguard the assets of, and eventually rewild, a whole ocean if present over-fishing trends continue. There is a logic to protecting Chagossian waters under any regime. The worry is that no one at the UN Court of Justice in the Hague or at the UN General Assembly in New York seems to have reflected on the case made by the 'father of biodiversity', the respected and loved global figure, Edward O. Wilson, recently deceased, that we need to protect half the land and half of the sea in order to tackle the extinction crisis and ensure the long-term health of our planet. Why would you not start by protecting one of the last great intact biodiversity hotspots of the Indian Ocean?

8

Enemies of Progress

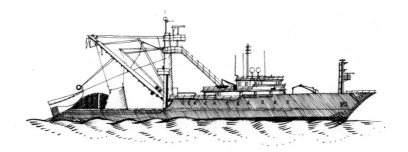

'The Belt and Road is a win-win initiative that calls for the participation of all nations based on the principles of extensive consultation, joint contribution and shared benefits, in the aim of achieving common prosperity. The Belt and Road is not a private path owned by a certain party but a sunshine boulevard shared by all.'

President Xi Jinping, China–UK Business Summit,
London, 21 October 2015

'When Xi says "I will fish" who can prevent him? If I send my marines to drive away the Chinese fishermen, I guarantee you not one of them will come home alive.'

President Rodrigo Duterte of the Philippines on
South China Sea, AP, July 2019

Conservation is a young discipline, younger than most techniques of exploitation. It is only now coming of age in the sea. So far in this book, we have looked at the flowerings of marine conservation in terms of the global expansion of protected areas over the past decade or so and the restoration of habitats at scale, and touched on at least one inspiring result of a slightly older discipline, ocean-wide fisheries management, in the bluefin story. We have examined the exciting potential for rewilding to bring back large marine animals, to restore seabed habitats and commercial fisheries and even to fight the effects of climate change on coral atolls and help them to survive into the next century (there's more about climate change to come). Now it is time to look at the forces that rewilding has arrayed against it: the forces of de-wilding, so no one can accuse us of being naive about what we are up against if we want healthy seas and to ensure the stability of the planet. These are the enemies of progress because it seems clear to me that they are damaging everyone, even themselves.

Aside from the measurements of climate change and pollution, the global indicator of the health of the seas is that 94 per cent of the world's commercial fish stocks are overfished or fished to their limits, according to the UN Food and Agriculture Organisation. You will note that the terminology avoids the fact that these are wild animals and you will search unsuccessfully in the official UN records for an estimation of the relative health of the marine ecosystems these 'stocks' live in. This is because the FAO recording system was set up merely to record catches of wild animals as human food. Even then, it mainly records the catches of large-scale industrial fishing fleets, which is a large but not exclusive percentage of the global marine catch.

We do know, however, who the main industrial fishing nations and blocs are. Those responsible for almost 50 per cent of fish landings globally – that is, the part of the fish catch that is put ashore rather than dumped back into the sea – are China, the European Union, Japan, Russia, Taiwan, South Korea and the United States. All of these countries subsidise fishing beyond what would otherwise be economically feasible, encouraging intense fishing by their fleets, which places stocks at risk, threatens the livelihoods of millions of people who fish, trade fish and depend on fish for food, and, critically, endangers the survival of our marine ecosystems and the health of our planet.

I am going to focus, for brevity, on the two whose landings are the largest: China and the European Union. China's stated landings in 2015 were four times the amount of any other nation and more than three times that of the EU's – if you believe China's statistics that is, which have historically been manipulated for political reasons. China's distant-water fishing fleet is sighted almost everywhere: trawling for krill within sight of penguin colonies in the Antarctic; fishing in a huge armada off the Galápagos marine reserve in the tropical Pacific;[1] jigging for squid in North Korean waters, to the extent that local fishermen starved;[2] trawling with licences granted by poor nations in the waters off West Africa and knocking on the doors of small nations in the Caribbean. When announcing that China was beginning commercial fishing operations for krill in 2015, an official used language from President Xi's 'Belt and Road Initiative' — a 'big idea' intended to create a belt of prosperity around a modern Silk Road, carrying goods back (of course) to China. He said: 'The Antarctic is a treasure house for all human beings and China should go there and share.'[3]

It is hardly unreasonable that the world's most populous nation is hungry for resources. The krill population of Antarctica is vast and still relatively unexploited, so China's hunger for it is theoretically not yet a problem. In practice, it is likely to have consequences for wildlife, particularly penguins, if it is caught in the wrong place. China's use of the word 'sharing' in international talks about krill, and elsewhere, does tend to imply that the largest share should go to the largest nation, which has some logic behind it. The consequences of 'sharing' in places where the waters are already overfished, though, and to the detriment of not just the sea life but the 'partner' country's own population, such as North Korea or in West Africa, are much more disturbing. Most controversial of all, China is taking fish species that were once part of the staple diet of local people and building fish plants that render them down into dust and oil, which is exported as feed to fish farms in China and as fish oil pills for consumers in the West. China's dewilding impact on the world's oceans makes it our first enemy of progress. It is such an egregious one that it is in danger of eclipsing other players — though they should not escape attention.

The European Union is the biggest single market for fish and fish products in the world. A measure of the effectiveness of the Common Fisheries Policy which applies in its home waters is that, as we have seen, four out of five stocks of cod shared with the UK and Norway have now collapsed. Fishing of those populations of cod continues at higher levels than is sustainable, by agreement, despite overfishing being supposedly made illegal by 2020 in the EU's own overhaul of that policy. With its home seas overfished – though probably not as much as China's – the European Union exports its demand to the world. Its distant-water fleet, mostly built on harmful subsidies – though these have supposedly now been abolished – fishes in West Africa, the Indian Ocean and the western Pacific.

In the Indian Ocean, the EU's distant-water tuna fleet is an unconscionable hangover from the colonial era. Morally, it is difficult to see why the European fleet is still fishing there at all – let alone taking the largest proportion of the catch when stocks there are overfished. The EU's distant-water fleet catches more tropical tuna – skipjack, yellowfin and bigeye – in the Indian Ocean than any individual coastal state, fish that are of huge economic importance to the local economies of those countries, though they are a drop in a bucket to the economies of Europe. The EU's purse-seine fleet, made up of vessels from Spain, France and Italy, bears an overwhelming burden of responsibility for the overfishing of bigeye and yellowfin tuna – and now for the not inconsiderable achievement of overshooting the official Indian Ocean catch limit for the once-innumerable skipjack, once called the cockroach of the sea.

Unusually in the Indian Ocean, the fishermen of many nations who were licensed to fish by the British authorities in Chagos waters until 2010, were every year required to report catches of threatened species. They duly reported the capture of thousands, including manta rays, blue and silky sharks. Sharks feed in the open ocean, depositing nitrogen around coral reefs in their faeces when they come inshore, which fertilises the coral.[4] This ecological function is apparently not a priority for the body that is supposed to manage the tuna fishery, the Indian Ocean Tuna Commission (IOTC), although it meets to discuss the extensive bycatch of endangered species, such as whales, turtles, sharks and other rare fish by tuna vessels and claims that progress has been made. Its own Working Party on Ecosystem and Bycatch, which meets every year, says that the available information of catches of these species is likely to be 'a severe underestimation', as most are discarded at sea and not reported. Were this data properly compiled it might horrify the tuna-eating public. That is why any discussion of rewilding that focuses on the Indian Ocean cannot ignore the activities of the off-shore tuna fishery. A few trends are going the right way in the oceans of the world but there are enemies of progress and the European distant-water fleet, comprising 250 vessels, is definitely one of these.

How, you might ask, did the EU's fleet grow as big as it did? There is a controversial link between China and the EU, in that growth of both fleets was associated with authoritarianism: in Europe then, in China now. The fleet the European Union was persuaded to take on from Spain at the time of accession in 1986 was the largest in Europe. It had been built up to that size, from the 1940s to the mid-1970s, by a well-documented policy of marine imperialism pursued under General Franco in what in Spain are euphemistically called the 'years of isolation' – when the fascist regime was cut off from the rest of the world.

Spain is still by far the largest catching country in the European Union's tuna fleet. It sets a poor example on reporting its catches, the data on which it manipulates at will. Much of what the EU/ Spain distant-water fleet does is contrary to the EU's own laws, which explicitly forbid overfishing, both at home and by its distant-water fleet. The EU Spanish fleet's vessels routinely overfish and frequently turn off their AIS satellite beacons, required under both EU and international law, for which they have not been penalised because the EU treats its fleet with the indulgence of a parent who has long since lost hope of controlling its undisciplined children.

The EU fleet in the Indian Ocean is larger than it looks. The Seychelles purse-seine fleet is Spanish and French owned and effectively an extension of the EU fleet, though it reports independently. There are also several French-owned vessels which fish under the Mauritius flag. Believe it or not, some of the Spanish tuna fisheries in the Indian Ocean have succeeded in applying for a certification of sustainability from the Marine Stewardship Council, undermining my faith in that organisation too.

To be scrupulously fair, Spain is by no means the only nation responsible for catching far more tuna than it should in the Indian Ocean. Coastal states such as Iran – which recently went on a piratical raid in Somalian waters – also shamelessly overfish their catch limits. In 2020, five years after the yellowfin tuna was discovered to be over-fished in the Indian Ocean, Oman increased its yellowfin catch by a shameful 85 per cent. The European fleet remains the biggest problem, though, because it catches the most fish, and overwhelmingly juveniles which is unsustainable as they have not had time to breed. It is surprising that within two decades of overfishing the bluefin to the point of near-extinction in another ocean, the EU's institutions appear to have learned none of the appropriate lessons.

As we have seen, the pole-and-line method of catching tuna practised mainly by the Maldives – India and Indonesia do fish using bait boats too, though nothing like on the same scale – is both fairer and ecologically more responsible than the longlines, purse-seine nets and drifting fish aggregation devices used by the industrial fleets. The pole-and-line fishermen have little bycatch, but they do land a high proportion of juvenile yellowfin, though this is utterly dwarfed by the number of immature fish taken by the sleek purse-seiners in luxuriously equipped fishing super-yachts. The proportion of juveniles caught by these European purse-seiners is estimated to be 97 per cent.[5]

One thing that would undoubtedly improve the survival of the yellowfin and other tuna species – and drastically reduce the bycatch of sharks, turtles and rare fish – is a reduction in the use of fish aggregation devices or 'FADs' dropped off into the Indian Ocean currents by a fleet of vessels that serve the purse-seiners. These drifting rafts of wood, plastic, netting and buoys, often topped by a satellite beacon, attract schools of tuna and other species which instinctively gather under flotsam. FADs are now the principal method used to catch tuna for canning. They are proliferating in the Atlantic too, in the Gulf of Guinea, catching the same tuna population fished by St Helena. Some tuna fleets, particularly the French, once used to set their nets on free swimming schools of tuna – sometimes around other species such as whales or manta rays which were allowed to escape. The advantage of this was that they at least caught more mature tuna which had reproduced once or twice. The unregulated FADs are estimated to cause the deaths of 500,000 to a million silky sharks a year across the oceans of the world. That is de-wilding on speed.

Despite the tuna industry's promises to switch to biodegradable materials, FADs – as well as contributing to the destruction of commercially targeted fish populations and those of other endangered species – still contribute a huge tonnage of plastic pollution to the sea as they wash up on shorelines and are broken down into smaller and smaller particles by the waves. Aldabra atoll, in the Seychelles archipelago, a UNESCO World Heritage Site famous for its near-pristine ecosystems and high numbers of seabirds, fish, sharks and turtle, has some of the world's highest tonnages of marine litter, mostly from FADs. The bycatch of slow-growing silky sharks, oceanic white-tip sharks and turtles in FAD fisheries, alongside the overfishing of the tuna themselves, makes the removal of drifting FADs a high priority if we are to maintain wildness, or biodiversity, in the oceans of the world. It deserves more focus by responsible nations who make pious promises about ocean protection and wring their hands about plastic pollution.

The European distant-water fleet, while causing great damage far from its home shores, is still dwarfed by China's distant-water fishing fleet, which is far larger than we thought. It is larger than even the Chinese thought. It is four times larger than even the Chinese government has said on the record that it wants it to be. In 2014, it was assumed in UN circles that the Chinese fleet numbered 3,432 vessels (nearly 14 times bigger than the European fleet). In 2020, the London-based Overseas Development Institute[6] reported that the Chinese distant-water fleet numbered at least 12,490 vessels and that nearly 17,000 vessels had the capacity to fish beyond Chinese waters.

The Chinese distant-water fleet is mainly a trawler fleet. The trawlers need to fish for bottom-dwelling fish on continental shelves rather than on the high seas where the Japanese and Taiwanese longline fleets target pelagic fish – those swimming in the upper layers of the sea. Historically, China trawled the Yellow Sea, between China and Korea, now one of the most overfished places on Earth. Having run out of fish there, China exported its trawlers to the world. Finding places to trawl means finding countries that will let the Chinese fish within their territorial waters, i.e. within 200 miles of the coast. The trouble began in Africa 20 years or so ago when the Chinese began to work through the existing system of trawler agents. These individuals tend to bypass officials in ministries and offer payments directly to ministers and senior officials to secure licences to fish – loopholes European fleets, mainly French and Spanish, had exploited before. Officials offer licences to fish in competition with their own, poorer, local fishermen, adding to pressure on already over-exploited stocks and continuing the unequal treatment of African nations, and Africans by other Africans, which harks back to the days of imperialism. As one Chinese diplomat told a European one: 'It's our turn now.'

Payments for fishing licences do spread largesse to gold-chain-wearing, Range-Rover-driving trawler agents in West African capitals but the trawlers bring little or no benefit to local people and they devastate the extraordinarily rich waters of the wind-driven West African upwelling, which brings nutrients to the surface that stimulate the growth of plankton and all other life, from fish to seabirds, across the wide West African continental shelf. The impact of catching already heavily depleted stocks is severe on fishing communities, where jobs often depend as much on processing fish as well as catching it. In Dakar, Senegal, many of the tables where the women used to dry fish in the sun now lie abandoned, a heartbreaking sight.

The Chinese trawler fleet would not be able to get to Africa, let alone fish there, without subsidies. The refuelling of Chinese trawlers fishing off West Africa is done by offshore vessels, a sure sign the fuel is subsidised – or simply pumped out by the state – provided that they are actually fishing. Local ports do not benefit from selling it to them. Trawler agents buy access to West African waters to fish stocks that have already been overfished by European and African vessels. Tragedy looms for them and for the Chinese skippers themselves, who are aware of their predicament if the fish run out, as they surely will. A friend asked one skipper what he and his fellow trawlermen would do: go on fishing until he caught the last fish, like they did in the Yellow Sea? The Chinese skipper nodded and said: 'Yes. We do not have the money to go back to China.'

The latest outposts of President Xi's Belt and Road Initiative are the fishmeal plants China has financed in West Africa. These plants export fishmeal – orange powder made from mashed up and cooked small fish – together with fish oil also used in fish feed, land animal feed and human food supplements, to Asia, Europe and the United States. In the Gambia, continental Africa's smallest country, Chinese trawlers and local wooden pirogues contribute an enormous 7,500 tons of fish a year to the Golden Lead (pronounced 'leed') plant, one of two fishmeal plants in the country which has only a 50-mile coastline. In both Mauritania and Senegal, the ability of the fishmeal plants to pay more than the local women would get from drying or smoking the fish and selling it locally has begun to break down the traditional economies of fishing communities, where the men used to fish and the women would sell the catch.

Greenpeace Africa found that more than half a million tonnes of small pelagic fish, such as sardinella, were being taken from the region each year. West Africa's production of fishmeal has grown tenfold in a decade, from 13,000 tonnes to more than 170,000 tonnes in 2019. Greenpeace counted 50 fishmeal and fish oil factories operating in Mauritania, Senegal and the Gambia, and reported that the industry was causing devastation in fishing communities. Human communities are starved of healthy food for the sake of farmed fish across the world, and processing plants have also been blamed for a rise in air pollution and contaminating waterways and the sea. You may have to contemplate that the next time you are tempted to purchase a fish oil supplement or farmed salmon.

Stocks of the small pelagics that feed the fishmeal plants are now failing in the absence of concerted regional management, according to the UN Food and Agriculture Organisation. Greenpeace Africa and a Netherlands-based organisation called Changing Markets are calling for a ban on fish fit for human consumption being used in fishmeal and for small-scale local fishermen and processors to be given formal legal status to protect the rights to their fish. They also want a 50 per cent reduction in industrial fishing in West Africa to allow stocks to recover.

What China is doing through its Belt and Road Initiative is evidently a new form of imperialism, though those who can usually be relied upon to criticise any form of colonialism have been curiously quiet about it. Aquaculture of a kind – oysters, mussels and vegetarian fish – can take the pressure off wild stocks. Carnivorous fish, on the other hand, consume many times more than they eventually supply to supermarkets and restaurants. The logic is that we should encourage people to eat the small pelagics, the flat and the round sardinella and the bongo shad, not boil them down to feed carnivorous fish such as farmed salmon and bass. And we should leave fish in the sea completely, rather than feed them to pigs and vegetarian fish like tilapia, as some Chinese fish farms now do to promote faster growth. These aquaculture and land farming methods are enemies of progress, and of fish in the sea.

There are plenty of alternatives to feeding fishmeal to farmed fish, including fly protein and feeds produced from fungi and bacteria, but right now the price of fishmeal is strong and so this questionable trade in brown dust is booming. The only hope is that European and American consumers will grow fussier about what their farmed fish is fed on. The Gambia's plants supply Norway which exports farmed salmon to the UK and the EU. Meanwhile, the association that represents the farmed salmon industry in Scotland states it does not 'currently use feed ingredients sourced from West African fisheries'. The word 'currently' is significant as the Scottish salmon industry says it intends to double in size by 2030. Where will the fish oil and meal come from?

In theory, of course, the world's wild-capture fisheries should be self-regulating. When fish stocks get low, fishing gets expensive and workers and investors move on. But in practice, unprofitable fleets often continue fishing because of the ultimate enemy of progress: subsidies. The greatest giver of state subsidies in the world, and hence the greatest enemy of progress in the oceans of the world, is China, which provides the greatest volume of harmful subsidies – the ones that cause overfishing – according to an analysis of who doles out the worst subsidies by the International Institute for Environment and Development. Harmful fishing subsidies take many forms but in China they can take the form of tax exemptions which can facilitate fishing in distant waters, including the high seas and the Exclusive Economic Zones of other countries, where it would otherwise be uneconomic to fish. China's annual subsidies for fishing come to $16.6 billion or 47 per cent of the global subsidy total and it directs the highest proportion to its distant-water fleet. The next down the list, for comparison, is the United States with $1 billion a year and a 2.9 per cent contribution to global subsidies. The European Union gives out $408 million in harmful subsidies per year.

The total global spend of $20–30 billion on subsidies of all kinds means that the world's fishing fleet is at least double the size the ocean can support, according to Rashid Sumaila of the University of British Columbia. Subsidies are hard to get rid of and have a long shadow: the vessels they build last a long time. Even though the European Union voted to bring an end to subsidies that cause over-fishing in 2008, when you look at the register of the tuna fishing vessels still fishing in the Indian Ocean belonging to companies in France and Spain, it is clear that many of them are boats built on subsidies handed out before that time. Not surprisingly, EU fisher-ies' interests are busy clamouring for the reintroduction of subsidies, presumably so their tuna fleet can be renewed.

The removal of subsidies at a global level is a necessity if the ocean's riches are to be protected. Conversations about ending fish-eries subsidies have been going on at the World Trade Organisation for 20 years. There is still hope of a conclusion to this discussion, which is the WTO's only outstanding negotiation requested by world leaders currently in progress. A great obstacle is how to treat developing countries, with a further obstacle that countries can self-identify as developing countries. China has self-identified as a developing nation for 20 years, even though it is now the world's largest economy with the largest distant-water fleet. We must continue to hope that an agreement will happen. A WTO agreement would bring the possibility of successive quasi-judicial challenges against fishing nations, via a disputes panel, and eventually a change in the paradigm towards unsubsidised fishing. Steaming across the world to catch somebody else's fish would become uneconomic, as well as unecological, and not before time.

If the future of fishing is artisanal, if all the good practice that has restored the seas in some regions is to be consolidated, then harmful subsidies have to go – and something will also have to be done about the Chinese trawl fleet. What will push the argument against continued subsidies this time is carbon – not just the emissions the fuel fishing fleets burn but that which is dredged up and released into the water column by trawlers, which then either finds its way into the atmosphere or prevents the ocean absorbing as much carbon as it otherwise would.

Understanding how carbon is released or absorbed by the ocean is a priority if we are to slow the rise in global temperatures. However, the potential for misreporting carbon emissions is huge. It is well to remember that China's reporting of its fish catches to the UN Food and Agriculture Organisation showed an increase in catches year on year until 2002, until analysis of the actual data showed for the first time that the world's wild fish catches were actually in decline because of overfishing and had been since 1989. Without the correct data, it is difficult to set targets and monitor the effect we are having on the planet.

We must include the impact of trawling – as well as other forms of fishing and whaling – in our understanding of man-made climate change if we are to influence the health of the oceans. But it promises to be a long haul.

9

Saving the Forests of the Sea

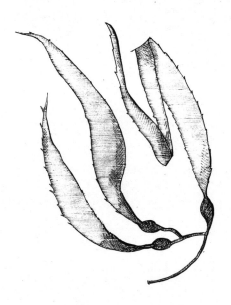

'I can only compare these great aquatic forests . . . with the terrestrial ones in the intertropical regions. Yet if in any country a forest was destroyed, I do not believe so nearly so many species of animals would perish as would here, from the destruction of kelp. Amidst the leaves of this plant numerous species of fish live, which nowhere else could find food or shelter; with their destruction the many cormorants and other fishing birds, the otters, seals and porpoise, would soon perish also; and lastly, the Fuegian . . . would . . . decrease in numbers and perhaps cease to exist.'

Charles Darwin, 1 June 1834, Tierra del Fuego, Chile,

The Voyage of the Beagle, 1839

'The climate crisis and the biodiversity crisis are really, and truly, inextricably linked. We not only need to solve the climate crisis in order to protect nature, we also must protect nature in order to solve the climate crisis.'

Al Gore, COP 26, Glasgow, November 2021

THE SUSSEX COAST

Chichester
Bognor
Littlehampton
Worthing
Shoreham

LONDON
Worthing
Brighton
ENGLISH CHANNEL

Kelp belt

B ognor, Sussex. The dives that made Eric Smith see red began on 17 April 2005. Eric is a spear fisherman, once a member of a national team, who has been free-diving off the Sussex coast since 1959. That day, the water had warmed up a bit and the visibility was good. He and his diving companion spotted the bream quickly from the surface because their moon-crater-shaped nests dug into the white chalk showed up clearly between the kelp fronds. The sea was alive with fish. The smaller bream were digging the hollows and the bigger fish were moving in to lay their eggs and challenging each other. Undulate rays were moving around the bed of kelp, feeding on the worms and small crustaceans disturbed by the bream. Shoals of large pollock drifted over the divers as they sank to the seabed and began to stalk their quarry. There were cuckoo wrasse nosing about and bass coming through in shoals, the largest of which Eric and his companion estimated at 8lbs in weight. These were really good fish. The two free divers ended the day with a couple of bass and two large bream and left feeling pleased to see so many fish. They intended to return on better tides to see what else they could catch.

Seven days later, the two divers started out at dawn. By the time they got to Bognor's promenade with their boat, two pair-trawlers could be seen towing a net between them out to sea at an angle alongside the main reef. When the divers slipped into the water 30 minutes later, they beheld a scene of devastation. The bream beds, so full of fish the week before, were wrecked and not a single large fish was to be seen. The crater rims of the beautifully dug bream nests had been flattened and there were large boulders in the middle of some of them. Torn kelp lay everywhere on the seabed and only a few very small bream could be seen trying to rebuild their nests.

When Eric was a child of 11 in Hove, the kelp was a thrilling brown-black forest that began a couple of hundred yards out from the shore. It conjured up all sorts of horrors for him and his mates. They imagined getting their limbs entangled in the three-foot fronds and being easy prey for giant squid and sharks. They would not swim over the kelp forest but swimming along the edge of it, they could see the tiny crustaceans and shrimps living within it. Between there and the shore, over the sandy shallows, teemed a nursery full of small and juvenile fish.

By the time he was 15, and a stronger swimmer, Eric decided to see how far the beds extended out to sea off Worthing. He found that the plants thinned out about one and a half miles from the shore. This was the area he calls the buffer, which protects not only the forest itself but keeps the force of the swell from smashing up the beaches further inshore.

In recent years, the waters off Sussex have become a featureless desert. More than 90 per cent of the kelp that was there in the 1950s has gone. Fishermen have blamed the great storm of 1987 for this and rising global temperatures, which disfavour some species of kelp, which are cold water species. But Eric points out that the kelp belt has been there for centuries and survived some enormous storms. Others have blamed the removal of raw sewage pipes, which they say used to fertilise the kelp. Eric points out that the profusion of bream spawning there fertilised the kelp long before the sewage pipes existed. He puts the blame for the damage to the kelp forest squarely on trawling. He and his late friend Mick Moore, another pioneer of diving and spear fishing, bore witness to many examples of kelp torn up and nursery areas for bream devastated. Eric was even told by a trawlerman that he had towed chains through the kelp to cut it. He and Mick saw how the trawlers had reduced College Rocks – a group of pinnacles in 35 feet of water off Shoreham that used to have conger eels living within them – to half the size. They saw how nets had festooned and damaged the many wrecks round which bass and cod used to shoal and now chains had been dragged through wrecks to scare the fish into nearby nets. All of this activity was entirely legal but deeply upsetting to Mick and Eric, who saw it as a case of fishermen destroying their own futures through greed.

Ten years of pressure from Eric and other local people outraged by what they saw has finally resulted in a proposal to ban trawling in the kelp forest by the Sussex Inshore Fisheries and Conservation Authority (IFCA). Its deputy chief executive, Sean Ashworth, was moved to act by the tide of evidence he saw that the trawlers had been making things worse for other fishermen and everyone else.

The day came for a hearing into the proposed bylaw at the IFCA's offices, where trawler owners and fish wholesalers spoke against the ban and conservationists spoke in favour. Then an old man with long grey hair down to his shoulders got to his feet. Eric, who was watching on a screen outside, said the old fellow was wearing a suit so worn and shiny that it must have been to a hundred funerals. He had a face the colour of tanned leather. Eric was expecting a typical trawlerman's response – but he was in for a surprise. The old man said that he would lose a lot of friends over this but he and the rest of the trawlermen had a lot to answer for, for the damage they had done over the years. He then referred to an article about what the kelp forest used to be like written by a spear fisherman called Eric Smith, which had made him remember his youth in the 1940s when you could go down to the water and scoop out the mackerel with a bucket. So the old guy voted for the ban, saying he owed it to his great grandchildren to try to rectify the damage he had caused.

The law was passed by a large majority but it then had to go before the Secretary of State for the Environment, George Eustice, for final approval. A long wait ensued. Key to the strong public support that had built up behind the trawling bylaw was a fine seven-minute film made by Sarah Cunliffe, a seasoned wildlife filmmaker who remembered how the kelp forests used to be from her final-year degree project, a marine life survey conducted by diving off Selsey in 1981. She persuaded Sir David Attenborough, who had shown an interest in preventing kelp forests being harvested in Scotland, to narrate it. Suddenly, the plight of the kelp was a national issue. The film was aired on the BBC's early evening news programme, *The One Show*, and on regional news during the public consultation in 2019. Eric's was no longer a lonely voice. Kelp was suddenly understood and the public rallied to save it. The #HelpOurKelp campaign, initiated by Sarah, who brought in Sussex Wildlife Trust and BLUE for the first official meeting of the Sussex Kelp Restoration Group before the film was aired in September 2019, mobilised 2,500 supporters behind a trawling ban.

Eric was moved to tears when a ban on trawling up to four kilometres off the Sussex coast was finally approved in February 2021.

Then, even he was surprised by the speed with which the kelp flourished in the first year of the trawl ban. Growing conditions were perfect: there was a long, cold, settled spell of spring weather with lots of sunlight. Eric and a younger friend, Steve Allnutt, started to dive in April. They found the first healthy plants at Bognor in an area Steve had been watching for five years, where a few plants had held on precariously within sight of trawler tracks. Now the kelp had exploded to an area 400 metres square with three species of healthy plants, some of them over 2 metres long. These they filmed and uploaded the footage to a Facebook page called Sussex Underwater. These were the first signs of revival.

Within two months, the kelp bed had erupted along a mile of inshore reef and was 600 metres wide. In the early spring, they also found three healthy kelp plants on the *Indiana*, a wreck off Worthing much altered by trawling activity. This was enough, Eric thought, to re-seed all the town's waters. Sure enough, six weeks later the three plants had increased to sixty. Meanwhile, the bream were back in force, covering an area three times that which had been seen the season before. Inshore fishermen reported some of their best catches ever. Cuttlefish were there too, trying to find fronds on which to lay their eggs, not always successfully as the eggs kept getting washed up. Pods of dolphins, not seen for a decade, were seen off Worthing pier. Eric and Steve also saw tope and smooth hounds, sharks up to five feet in length, chasing the bream. Later on, in mid-September, reports started coming in of vast shoals of whitebait throwing themselves onto beaches all along the Sussex coast, chased there by shoals of mackerel and bass. Wonderful things were happening that hadn't been seen since the 1950s and 1960s.

The speed of the revival in Sussex Bay had been little short of astonishing. That is down to the extraordinary dynamism of the kelp, a kind of macroalgae, not a plant, which creates some of the most diverse ecosystems on Earth. Kelp needs a hard substrate, usually rock, to hold on to, cool nutrient-rich water and light, lots of it. If it gets all these, there are species of giant kelp found in the Pacific that can grow 30–60cm a day. The main species found in Sussex, called tangle weed or *Laminaria hyperborea*, grows about 1cm a day up to a maximum length of 2.5 metres. Like oyster beds, kelp forests are extraordinarily rich habitats: over 1,000 species have been recorded in kelp forests around the UK.

As Sussex IFCA's impact assessment had already predicted, the advantages of restoring the kelp would be manifold. Besides more wildlife, which residents and tourists would enjoy, the coastal towns of Sussex would benefit from coastal protection during storms and the kelp would prevent the erosion of beaches that can cost millions to put right. Just in fishing terms alone, scientists commissioned by the IFCA calculated that the losses to the pair-trawling industry would almost immediately be matched by the increase in fortunes of the inshore pot and net fishermen. Fishing would not end, it would just be replaced by a less destructive kind; one small-boat fisherman in Bognor, Clive Mills, who gave up in 1999, recently went back to sea, knowing that his pots and nets would be safe and the sea more productive. That's a win–win.

But there may be a much bigger win for all of us. The most controversial gain of a restored kelp forest is carbon. It is controversial simply because no one knows how much carbon there is. We do know that kelp forest can take up to 20 times more carbon dioxide from the atmosphere than land-based forest. The question is then: where does it go? In winter, some of the kelp is washed up on to the beach by storms. Eric remembers farmers going onto the beaches and picking up the kelp which they used as fertiliser. Some of the kelp leaves or fronds are washed into deep water where they decay and become part of the sedimentary build-up of carbon in the deep sea. Then it grows again. You can measure the embodied biomass of a kelp forest and it is huge but no one knows where it all goes when it dies back. Some scientists have estimated that maybe 15 per cent is retained in the sea as net gain for carbon storage.

These uncertainties mean that the British government has yet to protect kelp, which is found along the south coast all the way to Cornwall, or to accept that it has a useful role in sequestrating carbon dioxide from the atmosphere. It is stuck in the old trap Sean Ashworth, formerly of Sussex IFCA, calls 'paralysis by analysis'. As he says: 'If you ban trawling and that leads to a more functioning ecosystem, you are improving biomass. Biomass is carbon. That is incontrovertible. There is net gain for carbon storage. We shouldn't not do it just because we do not know what the number is.' A child can see that protecting the kelp is the right thing to do but all the massed brainpower of the UK government's scientific advisers seems collectively unable to come to that same, obvious conclusion.

If the trawlers and dredgers managed to cause such mayhem in a kelp forest, it takes only a short leap of the imagination to think what they might be doing to the undersea forests of animals and plants out there in deeper water, on the seabed. Until recently, scientists only counted the carbon in the diesel fuel that fishing vessels burned. They had not looked at what the processes of trawling, dredging, mining and the development of wind farms and other structures were doing to bottom-living organisms on the continental shelves and the sediments that collect there and in the deep sea. The ocean floor is the world's largest carbon storehouse. It follows that if we stir up the mud and fell the forests that live on the rocky bottoms, we are likely to alter the amount of carbon reaching the atmosphere, either by preventing it being trapped by living creatures or by oxidising the sediments and making it harder for the sea to absorb carbon, which it does in vast quantities. The global ocean is estimated to have soaked up at least 40 per cent of man-made carbon dioxide emissions since the Industrial Revolution. It does this in multiple ways, from combining carbon dioxide with sea water at the surface during storms – which also accelerates the process called the acidification of the sea – to the growth and die-off plankton, plants, fish and other organisms that sink to the depths.

When we think of man-made climate change, we tend to think of coal smoke belching from chimneys, gas flaring from oil rigs, the logging and burning of rainforests and wide-bodied jets lumbering into the sky. Until recently, we did not think of trawlers and dredgers – and other forms of fishing or whaling that reduce the profusion of creatures in the sea. Yet the latest evidence suggests that these should be included in the mix of activities we should be discouraging if we want to hold the rise in global temperatures at less than an average of 1.5 degrees, which is the aim of the climate change treaty's Paris Agreement. Until now, the leaders of the trawling industry in the UK have been able to claim that the environmental impact of eating trawled white fish such as cod and haddock was lower than of eating tofu – because tofu is made of soya from cleared rainforest. Now, we have to consider the possibility that clearing rainforest and trawling are comparable activities.

The ground-breaking paper in *Nature* in early 2021 by Sala et al., which drew that conclusion, said that the carbon emissions from trawling globally were likely to be equivalent to the aviation industry. The data the study was based on were necessarily limited, as this subject had not been studied before and the conclusions about how the carbon is released into the atmosphere come from modelling, not measurements. But if these results are borne out by the usual process of scientific challenge and experiment, these scientists have discovered a huge hole in the world's carbon inventories and an entire missing chapter from the Intergovernmental Panel on Climate Change's list of ways of mitigating climate change. The potential for taking up more carbon in the sea by managing it more sensibly is clearly huge. But how huge? A high-level panel of scientists from 14 countries in 2018 concluded that ocean-based actions were capable of tackling up to a fifth of the mitigation needed to keep the global temperature rise to only 1.5 degrees Celsius.

Some of the stores of 'blue carbon' – carbon absorbed by plants and animals – in the ocean are already being included by some countries in their national plans to tackle climate change, known under the UN convention as 'nationally determined contributions'. Not by the British government, however.

Among the first things scientists tended to look at when they tried to define 'blue carbon' were mangroves – essentially coastal forests. Mangroves are estimated to soak up twice as much carbon every year as a tropical rainforest, yet they are being lost globally at a rate of 2 per cent a year to coastal development, especially in South-east Asia. They can, however, be regenerated or replanted.

Some seagrasses, mostly found in shallower water, are impressive soakers-up of carbon too. Posidonia, the Mediterranean seagrass variety, is estimated to absorb 15 times as much carbon as tropical forest per year. Posidonia is also in decline, so stopping that loss makes a lot of sense. Salt marshes, which are important for defending the coast against flooding, have recently been discovered to have a huge potential for soaking up carbon. Measurements taken at a scheme to create new salt marsh by allowing sea water to flood over the Steart peninsula in Somerset showed that it would take 100 years for a woodland to store as much carbon as Steart can store in six years. These findings indicate that the carbon storage potential of restoring salt marsh around the UK coast has been massively underestimated. Stopping the loss of coastal habitats and allowing more to be created as sea levels rise not only aids the rewilding of the sea but also tops the list of 'nature-based solutions' to climate change.

But coastal habitats such as marsh, seagrass and mangrove make up only 2.5 per cent of the ocean. The continental shelves amount to nearly 10 per cent and that is where most trawling activity takes place. There is a lot more work to do to eliminate the uncertainties in estimating the impact of trawling on the mud at the bottom of the sea. Some scientists say that the disturbance of sediments in UK waters could be equivalent to all emissions from oil and gas. Others say the emissions by trawling are trivial by comparison to the cultivation of terrestrial soils and methane emissions from livestock. At which end of the range lies the truth? It is estimated that regular trawling since the nineteenth century has reduced the carbon saved in the shallow seas around the UK, but what would it be like if these seabed habitats were protected? What would grow back? We simply don't know because we haven't tried it yet.

Some of the seabed is sand, where it is assumed that plants and animals would not grow densely or form 'forests of the sea' as they need harder ground. There are other places where there are already historic stores of carbon – pits, canyons and the deeper Scottish sea lochs. Then there is the submerged carbon that used to be above the waves. There are peat bogs on Dogger Bank that were drowned when the seas rose around 8,000 years ago. The Olsen *Piscatorial Atlas* of 1883 marks large areas of Dogger as having something called 'moorlog': peat. From skippers' records, we know that trawlers in the early years of the twentieth century used to pull up clumps of this peat, together with the remains of mammoth, rhinoceros and Palaeolithic hunting artefacts. How much is still down there? Is it not mad to strive enthusiastically to protect bogs on dry land but not peat in the sea?

It was with some incredulity that my colleagues and I left a Zoom call with the UK Department for the Environment, Food and Rural Affairs. We were told that there was no point in turning the protection of 4,600 square miles of Dogger Bank into an experimental carbon project because it was a sandbank and not much would grow there – even though it was a vast area. Carbon take-up, we were told, according to the government's best estimates, would be something like 1 per cent of the potential of changing methods used in terrestrial agriculture. Another official said that the UK did not want to compromise its 'world-leading position on climate change' by including blue carbon projects among its nationally determined contributions, as these might turn out to be 'hot air' – or fraudulent savings. A senior scientist said he was convinced there was good reason to protect Dogger Bank because of its 'biodiversity' but he could not bring himself to accept that there was a reason to protect it from trawling to save carbon at the same time, even though he conceded that this was likely to some degree. There would be better places to do this, he said, even though we all knew very well the government had no way of protecting them.

The officials seemed even more frightened by the possibility of allowing private sector companies to create 'carbon offsetting' schemes that would allow them to invest in carbon sequestration in an area such as Dogger. Some officials seemed to think that 'offsets' at sea could be a cheat which could allow major emitters to get out of their commitments – a fear which has some basis on land where some poorly monitored schemes have turned out to be forests that have been felled. There is, of course, a danger of offsetting schemes not working very well and the credits being bought up by big emitters of carbon dioxide as 'greenwash' so they can fraudulently evade their responsibilities. But if the carbon credits did not turn out to be real, would they not eventually be caught by the independent auditors brought in to certify them and people would ask for their money back? And in any case, if the objective was to save biodiversity at the same time as carbon, the benefits would be huge anyway, as with the Sussex kelp belt. There would be an assured benefit to nature while the carbon savings were measured over time. We simply could not understand why government was not capable of thinking about saving carbon and biodiversity simultaneously. Fundamentally, the government did not seem to agree with Al Gore's assertion that 'we must protect nature in order to solve the climate crisis.'

To date, the British government has yet to include any blue carbon projects in its 'nationally determined contributions'. Would it not show a more appropriate sense of urgency to start doing some of things to protect nature in the sea that they are already committed to anyway, and which are long overdue, and measure the carbon take-up as they went along?

Enough policy madness. Back to the sea. If we accept that it is a good idea to rewild the sea to maximise the amount of carbon it is capable of soaking up, we should not ignore the creatures that live within it. They too exist outside the world's carbon inventories but if they were included we would have to treat them very differently. The great whales were harpooned by the industrialised nations in their millions. Now the International Monetary Fund has estimated the value of a single great whale at $2 million and values the current stock of great whales at $1 trillion. This calculation is based on each whale's contribution to carbon capture, stimulating fish stocks and whale-watching tourism. The carbon ingredient of a whale's value is only partly in the whale's body itself – which if it dies naturally drops to the seafloor. The greatest value the whale imparts to the ocean is through the 'whale pump' – whales feed at depth and defecate at the surface when they come up for air, fertilising in the process populations of phytoplankton, one of the world's greatest sources of oxygen and a food for many species of fish. If whales were allowed to return to their pre-whaling numbers of 4–5 million – up from 1.3 million today – the IMF says they could capture 1.7 billion tonnes of CO_2 annually. That is roughly Russia's total annual emissions.

One of the most endangered great whales is the North Atlantic right whale – which, of course, got its name because it was the 'right whale' to hunt. In the early 2000s, efforts by the US and Canada to alter shipping lanes reduced whale strikes, by then the largest source of mortality, and numbers began to rise. Then warming waters led the whales to spend more time in the north, bringing them into conflict with the crab and lobster fisheries of New England and the Gulf of St Lawrence. A population which peaked at nearly 500 whales has fallen to 356 animals. The solution, apparently, is ropeless fishing technology, whatever that is, but the US authorities are not currently planning to require the fishing industry to transition to it. Around the world, more than 1,000 whales a year are still killed for commercial purposes – there is the killing of minke whales by industrial boats from Norway, Iceland and Japan and 'aboriginal' whaling of several species by indigenous people in Greenland, Alaska, Russia and the Caribbean – according to the World Wide Fund for Nature. It is time the climate change implications of that needless slaughter were properly considered.

Then there is the carbon embodied in fish. Unlike most terrestrial organisms, which release their carbon into the atmosphere after death, the carcasses of large marine fish sink and store carbon in the deep ocean. Yet fisheries have extracted a massive amount of this blue carbon and released nearly a billion metric tons of carbon dioxide to the atmosphere since 1950, according to one paper.[1] This is apparently less than half of 1 per cent of annual carbon dioxide emissions[2] but it is likely to be more significant when considered alongside the emissions of fleets catching the fish and the potential wider damage they have caused to carbon take-up in the sea. The paper showed that nearly half of the blue carbon extracted by fisheries in the high seas comes from fleets that would be unprofitable without subsidies. Therefore, the authors say, limiting the extraction of 'fish carbon' by fisheries in remote, unprofitable areas would reactivate a natural 'carbon pump' by allowing more big fish to die of natural causes and sink to the ocean floor.

All of this leads me to believe that the way fishing is managed could play a huge part in how the seas soak up carbon as well as making the ocean wilder. A study by researchers from Bournemouth University concluded that the overfishing of top ocean predators such as tuna, which we have seen over the decades since 1945, may amount to a loss of 10 per cent of the ocean's ability to sequester carbon. That is equivalent to 1 per cent of anthropogenic fossil fuel emissions per year – or the whole of, for example, Britain's or Poland's emissions. If that is true, then fisheries management is going to have to leave a lot more fish in the sea.

A critical role in the regulation of the climate is played by small, often strange-looking fish that live in the 'twilight' or mesopelagic zone, between 200 metres and 1,000 metres down. These fish are estimated to make up more than 90 per cent of the fish in the sea by weight. They undertake the largest daily migration on Earth, moving vertically upwards at night to feed in shallower waters above 200 metres and retreating to the ocean depths by day. Mesopelagic fish consume organic matter from surface waters which is then excreted at depths of 500–700 metres, transferring carbon to deep water. A pod of dolphins 10,000 strong was filmed demolishing a huge shoal of mesopelagic lanternfish trapped near the surface for the Netflix series *Our Planet*. Bluefin tuna like lanternfish too but they cannot find them alone; they use dolphins to find them. There is evidence that mesopelagic fish form a large part of the diet of other large predators, too, like deep-diving bigeye tuna, marlin and sharks. Mesopelagic fishes are estimated to play such an important role in carbon sequestration in the deep sea that without them, atmospheric CO_2 levels would be 50 per cent greater and global temperatures several degrees centigrade higher. They show, perhaps better than any other creature, why the fate of the oceans and the atmosphere are intimately connected and why overfishing is both a scourge of biodiversity and a driver of climate change.

Needless to say, the large abundance of mesopelagic fish is attracting growing interest from the fishing industry. So far, the difficulties of finding these small fish, catching them and processing them have luckily proved insurmountable. However, interest is stirring in the potential of these fish as sources of feed for farm animals and aquaculture. There have been four recent EU-funded international studies and one Norwegian research consortium looking at the development of mesopelagic fishing. Callum Roberts, professor of marine conservation at the University of Exeter, has called for a global moratorium on fishing in the twilight zone because of its potentially catastrophic consequences for the global climate and marine life.

There are, we now realise, huge global processes of carbon sequestration in the ocean which we interfere with at our peril and which we must hope will go on operating as efficiently as possible. This understanding will require enormous changes in what we currently consider to be permissible activities at sea. The good news is that we increasingly know that altering the way we currently catch fish on the continental shelves – just under 10 per cent of the total area of the oceans – could produce multiple dividends. The exciting thing, as the *Nature* paper authored by Sala et al. said, is that there could be a kind of triple win from stopping trawling and other damaging fishing activities: a win for climate, a win for biodiversity and a win for fish stocks, which could rebound if trawling was removed.

More science will no doubt have to be done to convince the fisheries authorities of the world of the blindingly obvious, which is that they have a responsibility, like everyone else, to promote carbon sequestration. They could, for example, manage fish populations, such as cod, for recovery, and to allow fish to grow as large as possible. At present, the authorities' best efforts amount to allowing commercially important species to bump along at a fraction of their historical size and abundance.

The controversial concept of maximum sustainable yield (MSY) is a common objective of fisheries management all over the world – though both in UK and the EU fisheries managers are failing to achieve it in practice, despite it being required under the UN Law of the Sea and by Sustainable Development Goal 14 (Life Below Water). The MSY concept describes the point beyond which fishing pressure reaches an unsustainable level, which can ultimately lead to stock collapse. Even if properly applied, the concept has been criticised for failing to include other pressures on fish, such as predation by other species or climate change. Economically, it makes little long-term sense to fish up to the maximum degree represented by MSY in seas that are already depleted, for that is not likely to allow the recovery of fish populations. Both economically and ecologically, it makes more sense to manage for maximum economic yield – the point at which it makes no more financial sense to put to sea, which happens sooner than MSY is reached. Those are the conventional arguments, often rehearsed, but I will add two more that are relevant if we are to rewild the seas. Both need to be taken into account if we want to tackle the climate and biodiversity crises, both largely ignored by the world of fisheries. Firstly, the objectives of fisheries management should be adjusted to take into account mankind's ambition to allow nature space for itself, ideally 30 per cent as this is becoming the commonly held target for the world's oceans by 2030. The total amount of fish, or marine animals, that an ocean holds should not therefore be assumed to be available for commercial exploitation; rather, 30 per cent should be deducted from the total if large-scale attempts at rewilding or protection are to have any meaning. Second, the potential of marine species to store carbon needs to be factored in when making management decisions about fisheries. It might make more sense to leave many species in the sea than to eat them.

Carbon is the biggest new reason to review and change how we exploit the sea since the advent of steam. It strengthens the already excellent economic case for protecting biodiversity and managing fish stocks better. What would the muddy North Sea be like if we managed it for biodiversity, fish and carbon – all at the same time? The only changes required would be the phasing out of trawling and dredging and the use of more targeted fishing technology – and, of course, stricter quotas on fish catches in the first instance as part of a plan for stock recovery and to leave more fish-carbon in the sea. What would the vast, once-rich West African upwelling – a dwindling resource for trawlers because of overfishing – be like if carbon was factored in to how it was managed? Might West African countries fight for the dollars shelled out by carbon offsetting schemes, rejecting the brown envelopes currently offered by some of China's trawl agents? That would be something to see.

Change is on its way. There are new, exciting, tangible connections being made between how we manage the oceans and the atmosphere. These connections should enable us to fix the biodiversity crisis and the climate crisis in a more joined-up way. Most importantly, we've begun to talk about bottom trawling and the subsidised distant-water fleets in the same breath and with the same pejorative tone as smokestack industries and coal-fired power stations.

10

The Future Could Be Wildly Different

'You cannot have a healthy planet without a healthy ocean.'

Peter Thomson, UN Special Envoy for the Ocean, 2021

'Humanity has been waging war against nature and it is time to make peace.'

António Guterres, UN Secretary-General, 2020

'This is scraping for a living – expensive, skilful and up to date scraping; but anxious and ill-rewarded – with every sign of being an effort contending with some invisible force of nature and economics – as men struggle on the edge of the Dustbowl, or cling to eastern American lands where forest is coming back. Yet nobody connected with near-water trawling would accept a hopeless view of it. Everyone persists because he knows the vast resources of the North Sea, the amazing recovery that the stocks showed in 1914–18, the fecundity and the rapid growth of fish. Nature here is not exhausted, only pressed too hard.'

'North Sea Scrapers', Michael Graham, *The Fish Gate*, 1943

L et me try to sum up the position in which we find our-selves: the health of our oceans, on which our own health ultimately depends, is in decline, partly due to greenhouse gas emissions. Year on year, the oceans of the world have acidified by a fraction, have less oxygen and are warmer. The warming is causing the death of coral, rising sea levels and changing the ocean currents. The ocean is also under pressure from pollution, in the form of plastics, though this is not the greatest ocean-based prob-lem. That is overfishing – mostly subsidised industrial fishing. It is destroying biodiversity, the resilience of habitats and robbing the world's poor of food. We now discover it may be having as much impact on the climate as the global aviation industry. Mangroves, seagrasses and kelp forests are still being destroyed, despite the fact that they soak up many times more carbon than forests on land. It is a pretty daunting litany of ills. A whole list of countries, industries and companies are being confronted for the first time by a new truth, that we have to address the problems of the oceans and the climate together: they are entwined.

The multi-million dollar question is whether we can do anything about ocean health; whether we have any chance of success. The only answer I can think of to the first question is that we need to rewild the sea. The answer to the second is that we need to do it in multiple ways that go far beyond the current comfort level of many countries, businesses and individuals. And we need to do it urgently.

Can it be done? From the evidence I have set out in this book, I believe the answer is yes. We must continue to join up the examples of success from around the world and the next decade is critical. We need new urgency and focus if we are to protect 30 per cent of the oceans, store carbon and find ways of eating seafood with a clear conscience.

Where will that urgency and focus come from? I believe it will surface from the steady trickle, becoming a pulse, of examples of where we have allowed nature in the sea some space to revive and have seen how it has rebounded. Remember: at the beginning of the last decade, the world had managed to protect just a little over 1 per cent of the oceans in any meaningful way and more fish stocks were in trouble. At the end of the 2010s, some 7.6 per cent of the oceans were under protection. It doesn't sound like much but these baby steps are changing the paradigm, for there is no longer just bad news coming in.

Another bulletin of good news arrived as I was sitting at my desk in Essex, a mile from the salt and ten miles as the crow flies from the port of Felixstowe, researching our next big adventure in saving the oceans. Up next was the possibility of helping to create a huge reserve in Baja California, Mexico. Mexico is not a country that I have been to but as I was talking to my new Mexican friends at COP 26 in Glasgow, I realised that my intrepid friend Rory Moore had been to the vast, remote offshore reserve that our friends had managed to get declared in 2017 – a great rectangle in the Pacific, the Revillagigedo Archipelago. On the satellite maps compiled by Global Fishing Watch, the rectangle appeared to be dark blue and entirely void of the small white dots denoting shipping or fishing activity. That absence was heartening.

Rory had been to the islands twice, the first time on a well-organised trip with the Scripps Institute in San Diego to tag oceanic manta rays. On that trip he came face to face with the largest tiger shark he had ever seen, or is likely to see, a monster five metres long with a head as wide as a whale shark. He said it was – funny how often this analogy comes up – like Jurassic Park. The next time he went, in 2011, was with a friend called Gaz on their ageing sailing boat. After long hours in hot Mexican offices securing their permits to enter the reserve. it took them four days to sail there from La Paz on the Baja peninsula. The Pacific swell was huge and landing was not permitted. Dropping anchor to dive around the jagged, rocky pinnacles that rose straight out of the sea was terrifying in its difficulty. Once below the waves, there were pods of dolphins swimming through silky sharks. Tiger sharks would appear out of the gloom, sending the heart thumping. Great formations of hammerheads gathered around the seamounts during the day. Huge trevallies charged around hunting baitfish near the surface. The manta rays were the oceanic kind – giants with a six-metre wingspan, like space-ships, and completely without fear. They would come to the divers and scan them with their sensory cephalic fins, which look like horns on each side of their broad heads. Whale sharks came and went. Huge tuna flashed past. All around, humpback whales were calling. Rory and Gaz saw nautilus, too, jetting up from the deep.

On the last dive, Rory was on a shallow coral seamount photographing a whale shark. There was a lot of shouting from Gaz on the surface. When Rory got back to the boat, Gaz was very pale and explained that a great white shark had been tailing Rory the whole time, which he had not noticed.

Having heard about the protection of the Revillagigedo Islands in 2017, I wanted to hear what had happened since Rory was there in 2011. I was delighted to make contact with James Ketchum, co-founder of a group called Pelagios Kakunjá, based in La Paz, which designed the reserve and was now monitoring it. The prohibition on fishing actually seemed to have worked and was being enforced by the Mexican navy which has a base one of the islands. There had been an unexpectedly rapid recovery in numbers of juvenile tuna in the middle of the reserve – though around Clarion Island to the west, illegal fishing activity was suspected. There had also been an increase in the numbers of silky sharks, a frequent bycatch in tuna fisheries, attracted by the profusion of smaller tuna. More silky sharks were migrating into the Gulf of California than had been seen for 25 years. This looked like a spillover effect from the reserve and was our segue into discussing a plan for a large reserve in the Gulf of California, too. Excitingly, after only a short time, nature was showing its usual dynamism when left to its own devices.

Hard on the heels of that news, we heard that, further south in the Eastern Tropical Pacific, Costa Rica, Panama, Colombia and Ecuador had just announced a new fishing-free reserve in all their waters, a corridor from the Galápagos to Cocos Island, to protect migrating turtles, whales, rays and sharks from foreign fishing fleets. In the list of developments that year, 2021, I might add that Chile was moving towards throwing salmon farms out of all marine protected areas – and Argentina has banned them altogether – long before we have got round to doing anything of the kind in the UK, Canada or the US. The number of cases of genuine rewilding in the sea around the world is ratcheting up year by year.

There could not be a greater contrast between the thrilling stories happening in the Eastern Tropical Pacific (and which we have witnessed ourselves across the British Overseas Territories) and what has happened to the sea off Lowestoft, the nearest big fishing port to where I live. The North Sea was once one of the most prolific seas in the world, famed for its fecundity and the rapid growth of its fish. Michael Graham's great book, *The Fish Gate*, published in 1943, explained how 'free fishing' – unlimited fishing – left the sea exhausted and the fleets failing economically at the start of the First World War and then again at the beginning of the Second. The two world wars have been called the First and Second Great Fishing Experiments – because they proved that overfishing was the cause of depletion before each conflagration and demonstrated that abundance returned when nature was left to its own devices.

In Lowestoft, fishermen are back in a similar place to before the war, having watched their fishing grounds destroyed by their Dutch neighbours dragging electric pulse trawls – now banned. They fear that, in a desperate race to catch something, the beam trawls will be replaced by super-efficient hydro trawls which substitute jets of water for electrical pulses to force the sole off the bottom and into the net. Lowestoft is the headquarters of fisheries science in England and, to add to the fishermen's woes, the scientists based at the government laboratory in the town seem to have messed up with their assessment of plaice. Even the Dutch beamers, to whom the local fleet owners sold out a few years ago, cannot catch their quota, let alone the small boats of the inshore fleet. The fish aren't there. We are back to Michael Graham's Great Law of Fishing: 'fishing that is not limited is unprofitable.' Fishing has not been limited enough.

What are the chances we could rewild the North Sea – or heavily used seas elsewhere – to somewhere approaching the fecundity of the Revillagigedo? It may seem a naive question but put it another way: what are the chances we could pull off the Third Great Fishing Experiment, entirely deliberately, by allowing nature to do its work on an exhausted sea? For that to happen, we would have to interfere with the freedom of the industrialised fleets to grind their way across the seabed, reducing species diversity, destroying wildness and stirring up carbon. If we were to do so, though, throughout our over-industrialised seas, might not the productivity of food actually be greater and there would be more employment, not less?

There is local support for this to happen. East Anglian coast fishermen have watched their grounds destroyed by the Dutch pulse trawl fleet – now back to beam trawling. They want the technological arms race to stop and for the sea to recover. They understand that trawling in the shallow southern North Sea will soon become more difficult anyway because of the proliferation of wind farms. They want to develop more selective fishing methods from lighter boats which do not churn up carbon on the seabed. Furthermore, these fishermen support a ban on trawling on Dogger Bank as they see protected areas as essential to nursing stocks back to health. Their community group is called Renaissance of East Anglian Fisheries (REAF) and, as an East Anglian born and bred, I am proud to support these small-scale fishermen in their ambitions.

Daniel Pauly, the great fisheries scientist, has argued – as I've alluded to previously in this book – that the future of fishing is arti-sanal. He sees the fishing fleets of the future as going out 40 miles at most and leaving the high seas as a bank to create fish and carbon. He believes that the days of the great subsidised fleets being allowed, in a laissez-faire way, to go on using their industrial killing machines across the oceans of the world are coming to an end.

The other thing we need if we are to rewild the sea is to hold governments to their stated ambition to deliver protection. It is out-rageous that an entire network of marine protected areas of various kinds has been devised and legally implemented in Europe, only for governments to allow a fleet of trawlers and dredgers to be literally driven through them. Exactly the same is true in the UK as in the waters of the European Union. When this is explained to the pub-lic, people are incredulous. We have industrialised the sea and lied about protecting it. Properly protected areas are the only thing that will begin the revival, which all would like to see. But protection must mean protection. The UK has achieved the protection of vast tracts of ocean in the Overseas Territories, with the co-operation of inspirational islanders who are more in tune with the needs of the sea and its creatures than we apparently are back home.

If the promised ban on trawling and dredging on Dogger Bank and in the other offshore 'protected' areas finally comes in, then we will have begun to bring it all back home. Just the removal of trawl-ing and dredging, if properly enforced, is likely to achieve huge benefits. Over time, this could lead to national parks in the sea, populated with the missing large animals – such as sharks, skate and sturgeon, as well as the recovery of fish stocks that fisheries man-agement has lamentably failed to achieve.

As I write, the British government is looking to enhance its protected area network with some new 'highly protected marine areas' (HPMAs) in English waters – no-take zones, where all fishing activity and extractive activity of any kind is banned. These will not be 'pilots', as ministers are describing them, for small no-take areas have existed around Lundy, Skomer, Flamborough Head and Lamlash Bay for years. In Lamlash, the protected area has become a nursery for cod and other fish utterly wiped out in the greater Clyde in the bycatch of the prawn trawlers. Just imagine if that recovery was allowed to expand. What is there to be so afraid of – except the wrath of a UK industry with a turnover smaller than Harrods department store?

It may be that too few of these 'no extractive use' reserves will be chosen and the already evident benefits of having them will have to be proved case-by-case over decades before we can have any more. While I believe our seas absolutely need many such highly protected marine areas – and I have faith that their benefits will exceed all expectations, not least to the fishing industry – my view is that greater gains are to be made immediately by expelling all destructive, bottom-towed fishing gears from protected areas and from everywhere within six miles of the shore.

Our two official systems – of fisheries management and feature-based marine conservation – are both broken. The first cannot seem to manage all stocks sustainably, let alone back to recovery. The second is heavily compromised. Managing the whole site, the whole ecosystem, throughout the water column and for a large area around, is now recognised as far better. But neither is a luxury. One senior government official said to me: 'I used to think that if you get fisheries management right you don't need protected areas. But in a sea with a mixed fishery and a lot going on, I think you do.' His point was that you need continually to factor in the ability of governments to let us down, scientists to get it wrong and fishermen to be just a bit better at catching fish than anyone could imagine.

Gradually, the message is getting through that unofficial conservation is beating official conservation at sea, as it does on land. In Lyme Bay, a marine protected area was lobbied for by the community long before it was delivered by government. Overseen on a whole-site basis by a voluntary committee, it has proved more effective in conserving fish than most official conservation areas or managed areas. The protected reefs of Lyme Bay have seen a fourfold increase in commercially targeted fish and a similar uplift in other species. The area protected from trawling and dredging is a gold mine, according to one fisherman. This creates the danger of a gold rush, which in turn will need managing, but the point is clear. If a marine reserve is so much more successful, economically as well as ecologically, than surrounding areas of the sea, should we not manage all inshore waters in this way, with a win for the fish, a win for the fishermen and a win for the wider community? That, in a nutshell, is the case for pushing trawling and dredging six miles out from the shore.

While we are about it, what should we do about trawling and dredging anywhere, not just near to the shore? There is a chorus from environmental groups to ban bottom-towed fishing gears altogether but as we have seen there can be perverse impacts of banning them and allowing a proliferation of other fishing methods. At present, a small dredge is the only known way of harvesting oysters – so where do you draw the line? It is important to remember the principle at stake, which is that the fishing industry should have to consider the environmental impact of what it does and seek to minimise it as other industries do. (I remember the head of a power company who had spent years seeking permission to lay a cable on the seabed watching astonished as a fleet of scallop dredgers tore up the bottom on a parallel course without having to ask anyone's permission.) The freedom to trawl or dredge impacts on the rights of others, like the freedom to carry a gun or, as those in former ages did, to send children up chimneys or keep slaves. As Edmund Burke, a leading contemporary opponent of the slave trade, put it: 'What is liberty without wisdom and without virtue? It is the greatest of all possible evils.' If we were wise about how we exploited the sea trawling would be the last method allowed.

We must, of course be realistic. Would we be able to catch sole or cod or harvest scallops without trawls or dredges? Yes, I think we would. Soles used to be caught on lines before trawlers came along. Scallops can be dived for and there are other techniques under development, such as potting. Would it be more expensive to fish in more sustainable ways? Perhaps, but fish and shellfish are now an expensive luxury. Quality, not price, drives purchasing decisions on the docks. Fishing should pay its environmental costs and pass these on to the consumer. We should grow the coastal and fishing businesses of the UK by investing in our natural capital. The way you invest in a wild ecosystem is by leaving it alone at every opportunity, and some of it permanently.

There are those in the fishing community who know this very well. They want us to be more ambitious in holding out for recovery and restricting the most damaging methods and are ever vigilant for arguments based on short-sightedness and greed. As this book has shown, determined people have tried and succeeded in some remote and amazing places and also in some quite close to home. We must hand it to Dave Sales and his working successors in Lyme Bay, to Otto, Waylon and Julie Thomas from St Helena, to the entire population of Tristan da Cunha and Ascension, to the campaigners of Lamlash Bay, to the fishermen of the Isle of Skye's Inner Sound, to the inshore fishermen of East Anglia, to Eric Smith and his observation of kelp over 60 years. Thank you all for showing us such an example of how to protect what is still wild and address the degraded reality that exists off our shores.

Eric Smith said to me: 'I want the sea back as I had it in my youth.' Is that such an unrealistic expectation? I really don't think so. In the mouth of an old man who has lived for three generation-spans so far, that sounds very like the same aspiration as Gro Harlem Brundtland's definition of sustainable development: 'Development that meets the needs of the present without compromising the ability of future generations to meet their own needs.' We know now how to rewild the sea. We just need to look to the proliferating examples of success. Who will stand in the way?

With a changing climate, we can never completely restore the seas of the past exactly as they were but we can have profusion: the return of great whales and slow-growing giant fish, an abundance of the baitfish they and the seabirds feed upon, not to mention myriad wonderful seabed ecosystems, such as the Sussex kelp, soaking up vastly more carbon from the atmosphere. To do so, we will just need to trust nature a little more and invest in the natural world in the only way we can, by being a little more prepared to leave it alone. If we follow the growing number of successes which are beginning to stack up around the world, who knows where they might lead? Remember the lyric Ian Tyson wrote in the song Neil Young sang? 'Four strong winds that blow lonely, Seven seas that run high, All those things that don't change, come what may.' Actually, the seas do change, in ways that we can influence, whatever the song might say.

ACKNOWLEDGEMENTS

I suppose I might have written another book a lot sooner after *The End of the Line* (published in 2004) if that book had not led to a film, and then to the start of Blue Marine Foundation. It was our present chairman of trustees, Arlo Brady, who encouraged me to put ink to paper again in the tenth year of our charity's existence. Two years on, now the book is written, those storylines have got stronger, as have the tendrils of hope out there in the oceans. There is more to celebrate, as well as some obvious disappointments, such as Britain's failure to make a better job of its post Brexit fisheries legislation.

A book is a very personal thing and writing it takes the greatest toll on the people closest to you, so the principal person who deserves thanks and praise for this book happening at all is my wife, Pamela, who read all of it several times, made it make sense, put up with me, ensured the worst versions never saw the light of day and took over the whole visual side of the enterprise. I feel particularly privileged, having been edited by hundreds of people over my career as a professional journalist, to have been edited by Drummond Moir and his team at Ebury – who took a splendidly clear view and offered the easiest-to-take advice, for which huge thanks. It was a delight not only to work with the gifted illustrator Emily Faccini but also to discover we had so much in common in the West of Scotland. My agent, Ivan Mulcahy, is no slouch at editing himself and deserves belated thanks for making the original proposal of *The End of the Line* something so strong that it provoked a bidding war, meaning I could afford to write it. Thanks to their support for my previous book, this present one had the formidable support, in one way or another, of Stephen Fry, Margaret Atwood, George Monbiot, Lewis Pugh and Isabella Tree from the proposal stage. I am profoundly grateful for their confidence in me, I hope it has been borne out by the result.

This account of positive developments in the oceans of the world would not have been written without, first, the team that made *The End of the Line* into a wonderful film, directed by Rupert Murray; and, second, George Duffield and Chris Gorell Barnes, part of that team, who decided to set up BLUE, and then worked for it tirelessly, for nothing, for 12 years. My story is BLUE's story – but I must emphasise that this book is entirely based on my own individual opinions and not an official document. I would, however, like to pay tribute to all those mentioned in this book who helped to bring some of our campaigns and projects to a conclusion, and those who are pursuing enterprises that are ongoing. I offer my thanks to my colleagues at BLUE who are mentioned in the book. Some deserve special thanks for their help: Clare Brook for encouraging me to take time off and teaching me I am not indispensable; Dan Crockett for allowing me to use the title of an inspiring conference he devised as the title of this book.

I am grateful to those who read and offered comments on the text: George Duffield, Clare Brook, Jude Brown, Tom Appleby, Callum Roberts, Luke Helmer, Priyal Bunwaree, Shaha Hashim, Vivienne Evans, David Tudor, Rodney Anderson and Tim Glover. Rory Moore deserves a special mention for telling me so many of his adventures that are actually in the book. I am grateful to other witnesses for their accounts and advice: Tom Horton for his story of first seeing the bluefin in British waters; Jonathan Hall from the RSPB, a great ally in the conservation world, for his recollections of the islands of Tristan da Cunha. Thanks, also, to all his colleagues in the Great British Oceans coalition, one of the most successful conservation coalitions on Earth. I am grateful also to Philine zu Ermgassen and Jo Preston for vastly enhancing my knowledge of oysters, Heather Koldewey for her scientific knowledge of the Chagos and Terri Portmann for good advice on many subjects which I nearly always take.

Last but not least I must thank the people this book is actually about, the users of the sea who have done so much for conservation. I must thank the late Dave Sales and his wife Gill for making so much of their time available and for sharing with me a lifetime of wisdom and experience about fishing, not all of which I managed to shoehorn into this book. There are other wonderful stories I aim to make use of one day. I would like, again, to thank the fishermen of Lyme Bay. I would like to salute the fishermen of St Helena and their leader, Waylon Thomas, who helped me with the story of his father, Otto. And I would like to thank Eric Smith for giving me his accounts of the decline – and return – of the Sussex kelp and Sarah Cunliffe for introducing him to me and making a wonderful film. May his algae spread and his bass and bream grow more numerous.

If I have forgotten anyone, please forgive the confusion that overcomes one, along with exhaustion, when one writes the final full stop. Thanks to every one of you who has shared my journey, for bringing the oceans of the world one of its rarer commodities: hope.

Charles Clover
Dedham, Essex
2022

References

Introduction: Return of the Giants

1. Neil Young, solo album, *Comes a Time*, 1978
2. 'Ocean' or 'oceans'?: There is a movement within marine science circles when referring to the oceans to drop the 's' and always refer to 'the ocean'. Singular it absolutely is in the sense of connectivity. Waters circulate around the Earth driven by temperature and salinity on an ocean conveyor belt, which threatens to slow down because of climate change. Thus, it is entirely right to refer to 'the ocean' in an oceanographical context or when referring to global warming.

   However, in common parlance and in literature, there are oceans and it is the sea and there is every reason to think matters will remain so. I do not think it is right to insist on this fashionable singular, 'the ocean', in a conservation context either. In terms of species diversity, the oceans are broadly distinct. In law, too, there is the UN Law of the Sea but there are also specific conventions or treaties that apply to particular oceans. It is misleading, then, always to talk about 'the ocean' as a single entity. So in this book I will use both terms, single and plural, in ways that have evolved for good reason. You can't call for measures to 'save the ocean'. It sounds absurdly unachievable. It is like calling for 'world peace'. We should celebrate the fact that we can take actions locally and regionally that make our oceans better managed than elsewhere – and create competition between nations in doing so. We need to think globally but we need to act locally, particularly when it comes to the oceans.

Chapter 1: Where the Wild Things Really Are

1. Account of Ruth Thurstan's research taken from *Ocean of Life*, Callum Roberts, Penguin, 2012
2. 'The Location and Protection Status of Earth's Diminishing Marine Wilderness', Kendall R. Jones et al., *Current Biology*, vol. 28, no. 16, 2018

Chapter 2: If In Doubt, Think Big

1. See *The End of the Line*, Ebury Press, 2004, p. 144. The 50 per cent illegal catch figure for cod was taken from an interview with Harry Koster, head of the European Commission's fisheries inspectorate in Brussels and from a Commission press release at the time. I commented: 'Just as many of Europe's fish stocks are in danger of irreversible decline: every other cod, every other hake that hits your plate is stolen, from the general public and their grandchildren, the rightful owners of the sea. All because no one has the political courage to enforce the rules now that fish stocks are low.'
2. 'Catch reconstructions reveal that global marine fisheries catches are higher than reported and declining', Daniel Pauly and Dirk Zeller, *Nature Communications*, 19 January 2016
3. The 'asks' in the closing cards of *The End of the Line* were:
   Ask before you buy. Only eat sustainable seafood.
   Tell politicians: respect the science, cut the fishing fleet.
   Join the campaign for marine protected areas and responsible fishing.
4. 'Chagos: A History – Exploration, Exploitation, Expulsion', Nigel Wenban-Smith and Marina Carter, Chagos Conservation Trust, 2016
   'Cast Away' – a review of the above by Charles Clover, *Resurgence and the Ecologist*, no. 304, September/October 2017

Chapter 3: The Battle for England's Coral Garden

A note on the history of marine protection.

1. Until the present century, attempts to protect important wildlife habitats and species in British waters were limited and largely unsuccessful. Voluntary marine reserves were created by local wildlife trusts in the 1970s around such places as Lundy Island (off Devon), Skomer (Pembrokeshire) and St Abb's Head (Berwickshire). These were not always respected by the

fishing industry. A provision for statutory reserves was included in the Wildlife and Countryside Act 1981. The first sites were chosen for no apparently good reason and failed to include any charismatic animals that the public would understand needed protecting. Understandably, when the first statutory reserve was imposed in Scotland, in Loch Sween, there was a revolt locally. Further attempts to find ways to protect rare marine habitats and species were made in the 1990s, through the EU Habitats and Species Directive. These were more successful, but were based on protecting features, not whole ecosystems with all the creatures that lived in them. The core area of Lyme Bay's reefs was given protection under European legislation a couple of years after the Statutory Instrument was first imposed by Jonathan Shaw in 2008. Other stretches of reef, such as the Stennis Ledges, an area of rocky ground off Chesil Beach, were added under new national legislation, the Marine and Coastal Access Act 2009, which set up another far weaker national protection vehicle, Marine Conservation Zones. There was nothing to say what fishing methods were to be prohibited, no criteria for restoration and no way you could use the law to go against the government or statutory bodies to ensure they adhered to the spirit of the Act. There was an elaborate public consultation which allowed the public to decide where highly protected areas – known as reference areas – would go, which resulted in none being created. Richard Benyon, MP, who was the Opposition's spokesman on fishing when the Bill went through, told me that in retrospect he wished he had torn up the Marine and Coastal Access Act when he became minister in 2010. Public expectations were higher than what the government machine and its inward-looking and terrestrially minded conservation bodies actually achieved. To his credit, Benyon returned to finish the job from the back-benches by chairing a panel on the creation of Highly Protected Marine Areas, which made recommendations that at least five of these be designated as a first tranche.

2. 'Marine Protected Area status can boost fish populations by almost 400 per cent', Alan Williams, University of Plymouth, 9 September 2021
   More on Lyme Bay in the Science pages and Research Report downloads on the Lyme Bay Fisheries and Conservation Reserve website.
   'Ecosystem Approach to Fisheries Management works – how switching from mobile to static fishing gear improves populations of fished and non-fished species inside a marine protected area', Bede F.R. Davies, Luke

Holmes, Adam Rees, Martin J. Attrill, Amy Y. Cartwright, Emma V. Sheehan, *Journal of Applied Ecology*, 8 September 2021

Chapter 4: Return of the Native (Oyster)

1. Confusingly, the Pacific oyster is often known commercially as the Portuguese oyster. This is because a species found in Portugal, *Crassostrea angulata*, is very similar but genetically distinct. The World Register of Marine Species (WoRMS) says that from all recent studies it seems clear that the European strain of *C. angulata* was introduced to Portugal in the sixteenth or seventeenth centuries from Taiwan. It is very similar to, but can be recognised genetically from, *C. gigas*, introduced later from Japan.
2. *The Big Oyster: History on the Half Shell*, Mark Kurlansky, Random House, 2006
3. 'The History and Decline of *Ostrea lurida* in Willapa Bay, Washington', Brady Blake and Philine S.E. zu Ermgassen, *Journal of Shellfish Research*, vol. 34, no. 2, 2015
4. 'Loss of an Ecological Baseline through the Eradication of Oyster Reefs from Coastal Ecosystems and Human Memory', Heidi K. Alleway and Sean D. Connell, *Conservation Biology*, 22 June 2014
5. '*Ostrea edulis* Beds in the Central North Sea: Delineation, Ecology, and Restoration', Floris P. Bennema, Georg H. Engelhard and Han Lindeboom, *ICES Journal of Marine Science*, August 2020

Chapter 5: Jurassic Parks of the Sea

1. *Fragments of Paradise: Guide for Conservation Action in the UK Dependant Territories*, Sara Oldfield, Pisces Publications, 1987
2. The target, known as Aichi target 11, calling for 10 per cent of the global ocean, was set as a supplementary agreement to the UN Convention on Biological Diversity agreed at Nagoya in Japan in 2009. A UK initiative called the Global Ocean Alliance is now calling for the next global target to be 30 per cent of the ocean, based on scientific evidence that this is the minimum required to protect its biodiversity, but scientists say that up to 70 per cent of the ocean could very well be needed to preserve the stability of the planet – *see* 'A review of Evidence for Area-based Conservation Targets for the Post-2020 Global Biodiversity Framework', Stephen Woodley,

Harvey Locke, Dan Laffoley, Kathy MacKinnon, Trevor Sandwich, Jane Smart, *Parks Journal*, November 2019

3. The International Union for Conservation of Nature is the global authority on the status of the natural world and the measures needed to safeguard it. It has six categories of protected area, with resource use permitted only in Category VI 'Protected area with sustainable use of natural resources'. Low-level non-industrial use of natural resources compatible with nature conservation is one of the main aims. The British government states that its management of South Georgia, which allows industrial fishing for toothfish and krill, fits the criteria of a Category VI protected area. Not all agree. But it is hard to see how one might fish with 'low-level, non-industrial vessels' in seas as huge as these: practically speaking, the focus needs to be on the sustainability of the catch.

4. The *Journal of the Marine Biological Association*, vol. 97, no. 4 (Ascension Island), June 2017, is a special issue containing 20 papers on the island's marine biodiversity. It also reported on the results of an expedition by the RSS *James Clark Ross*, which mapped the seabed down to 1,000 metres around the island, finding one species of algae and two sea slugs new to science: www.south-atlantic-research.org/ascension-island-special-issue/

5. '100 million sharks killed each year, say scientists', Press Association, *Guardian*, 1 March 2013

6. Provided by Fishlove.

7. The UKOTs represent 28.3 per cent of the global total of implemented fully or highly protected areas according to the Marine Protection Atlas compiled by the Marine Conservation Institute. That does not include St Helena because it does not qualify according to the Institute's criteria as highly protected.

Chapter 6: Dinosaurs of the Dogger

1. 'Elevated trawling inside protected areas undermines conservation outcomes in global fishing hot spot', Manuel Dureuil, Kristina Boerder, Kirsti A. Burnett, Rainer Froese, Boris Worm, *Science*, 21 December 2018

2. An independent document published by the British government in summer 2021

3. 'Marine strategy part one: UK updated assessment and Good Environmental Status', Defra, 2019

Chapter 7: Paradise Lost?

1. 'Coral reef islands can accrete vertically in response to sea level rise', Gerd Masselink, Eddie Beetham and Paul Kench, *Science Advances*, 10 June 2020
2. 'Coastal flooding could save atoll islands from rising seas – but only if their reefs remain healthy', Gerd Massellink and Paul Simon Kench, *The Conversation*, 16 September 2021
3. 'A review of a decade of lessons from one of the world's largest MPAs: conservation gains and key challenges' Graeme C. Hays, Heather J. Koldewey, et al., *Marine Biology*, 14 October 2020
4. 'Maldives embroiled in Mauritius-UK tussle over Chagos', Ahmed Mujuthaba and David Brewster, *The Interpreter*, The Lowy Institute, 8 December 2021
5. 'Chagossian exiles celebrate emotional return as UK tries to justify control', Owen Bowcott and Bruno Rinvolucri, *Guardian*, 20 February 2022
6. 'Islanders expelled by Britain return 50 years on with anger still burning', Christina Lamb, *Sunday Times*, 13 February 2022
7. 'Chagossians fear being booted from UK 50 years after they were removed from own islands', Jack Clover, *Sunday Mirror*, 19 February 2022
8. The Republic of Mauritius has committed to achieving the UN Sustainable Development Goal 14.5 of achieving 10 per cent of its coastal and marine waters within protected areas by 2020. Currently, 0.009 per cent of its coastal and marine areas are under protection, according to the Nairobi Convention. nairobiconvention.org/clearinghouse/node/421
9. 'It is time for Britain to abandon its "unsinkable aircraft carrier" in the Indian Ocean', David Snoxell, *Conservative Home*, 4 January 2022

Additional reading:
Reef Life: An Underwater Memoir, Callum Roberts, Profile Books, 2021

Chapter 8: Enemies of Progress

1. 'Chinese fishing armada plundered waters around Galápagos, data shows', Dan Collyns, *Guardian*, 17 September 2020
2. 'Licence to Krill', Greenpeace report, 12 March 2018
3. 'Mobile marine predators: an understudied source of nutrients to coral reefs in an unfished atoll', Jessica J. Williams, Yannis P. Papastamatiou, Jennifer

E. Caselle, Darcy Bradley, David M.P. Jacoby, *Proceedings of the Royal Society B*, 21 March 2018

4. 'Paradise Lost: the marine pollution of Aldabra Atoll, Seychelles', *Loupe* (Christopher Ward magazine), no. 22, October 2021

5. 'The 2020 Annual Report on the EU Fishing Fleet (STECF 20-06)'

6. 'China's distant-water fishing fleet: scale, impact and governance', Miren Gutiérrez, Guy Jobbins et al., Overseas Development Institute, 2 June 2020

Additional reading:

'The past, present and future use of drifting fish aggregating devices (FADs) in the Indian Ocean', Tim K. Davies, Chris C. Mees, E.J. Milner-Gulland, *Marine Policy*, vol. 45, March 2014

'The deadly secret of China's invisible armada', Ian Urbina, *NBC News*, 22 July 2020

'Fish farming is feeding the globe. What's the cost for the locals?', Ian Urbina, *New Yorker*, 8 March 2021

'Stop selling fish raised on fishmeal from West Africa, supermarkets told', Tess de La Mare, *Evening Standard*, 1 June 2021

'Mealy Deal', Beatrice Gorez, *Samudra Report*, no. 78, January 2018

'The cost of harmful fishing subsidies', Robert Arthur, Stephanie Hayward, John Pearce, William Sharkey, IIED/MRAG working paper, March 2019

Chapter 9: Saving the Forests of the Sea

1. 'Let More Big Fish Sink: Fisheries prevent blue carbon sequestration – half in unprofitable areas', Gaël Mariani et al., *Science Advances*, October 2020

2. The International Energy Agency says that carbon dioxide emissions reached 33.1 billion metric tonnes, or gigatons, in 2018

Additional reading:

'The potential for mobile demersal fishing to reduce carbon storage and sequestration in seabed sediments', Graham Epstein, Callum Roberts et al., *Global Change Biology*, February 2022. https://doi.org/10.1111/gcb.16105

'Entering the twilight zone: The ecological role and importance of mesopelagic fishes', Callum Roberts, Julie P. Hawkins et al., Blue Marine Foundation, December 2020

UK Parliament Postnote 651 Blue Carbon

'Protecting and effectively managing blue carbon ecosystems to realise the full value to society – a sea of opportunities', Dan Laffoley, World Wildlife Fund, November 2020

Index

University of Portsmouth 85, 88, 92, 96, 98
US National Fish and Wildlife Foundation 94–5

Vera, Frans 17

Waldegrave, William 29
Walton, Izaak: *The Compleat Angler* 25
Washington State Department of Fish and Wildlife 91
Watson, Dr Bob 72
Webster, Michael 169
Wells, Colin 118
whale pump 215
whale shark 128–30, 131, 136, 168, 229
whaling 9, 154, 197, 210, 215, 216
whole site approach 20, 76, 234, 235
wildlife trusts 53, 55, 65, 66, 68, 69, 75, 206

wildness of the sea 5–22
Willapa Bay 91
Wilson, Edward O. 114, 177; *Half-Earth: Our Planet's Fight for Life* 105
Wolfe, Mandy 73
wolves, reintroductions of 15–16
World Oceans Day 123
World Trade Organisation (WTO) 195–6
World Wide Fund for Nature (WWF) 37, 38–9, 216
Wye, River 31

Xi Jinping 181, 185, 192

yellowback fusilier 171
yellowfin tuna 111, 112, 113, 114, 121, 132, 186, 188, 189
Yellowstone Park 15–16
Young, Neil xvii, 238